# RAMAYANA
## FOR
Exercises at the end

2 in 1

# CHILDREN

### Vatsala Iyengar

🌐 **Vasan Publications**

Rs. 75/-

© Vasan publications,
Edition : 2013

*Published by:*
**Vasan Publications**

# 25,  Vasan Towers, Goods Shed Road,
Bangalore - 560 053,  Ph.080- 2670 5679
e-mail : info@mastermindbooks.com
www.mastermindbooks.com

D.T.P :
Sunshine

Printed at:
Srinidhi Graphics

# CONTENTS

THE BIRTH OF RAMA............................................. 5

THE VALIANT PRINCES....................................... 8

SITA'S SWAYAMVAR............................................ 17

KAIKEYI AND HER WISHES............................... 24

THE DEMONS IN THE FORESTS....................... 62

THE KIDNAPPING OF SITA............................... 75

RAMA SEARCHES FOR SITA............................. 86

THE LAND OF THE MONKEYS........................... 91

HANUMAN MEETS SITA—
    LANKA IS DESTROYED.................................... 103

THE WAR.............................................................. 114

# THE BIRTH OF RAMA

Ayodhya was a magnificent city on the banks of the river Sarayu in Kosala kingdom. It had wide roads, huge buildings, beautiful parks and glittering shops. The people of the city lived a happy and contented life as they were ruled by a noble king called Dasharatha, who cared for his people very deeply.

King Dasharatha had three wives—Kaushalya, Sumitra and Kaikeyi. Kaushalya was the eldest queen. Though the king loved all his queens deeply, it was Kaikeyi, his youngest queen, who was his favourite. But in spite of leading such a good life, Dasharatha was still unhappy. This was because he had no children. He was getting old and had no son to ascend the throne.

Unable to see the king being sad, the sages advised him to perform a Yagna and pray for children. Heeding to their advice, he performed the Yagna. Pleased with him, 'Agni' the Fire God, emerged out of the firepit, handed over a cup containing sweetened milk to the king and told him, "O King! This kheer is the nectar of life. It was prepared by the Gods in heaven. Distribute it among your wives. You will soon be blessed with sons." Dasharatha was delighted. He thanked Agni for this boon. He then gave Kaushalya half of the kheer. He divided the remaining kheer into two portions and gave one portion to Sumitra and the other one to Kaikeyi.

Subsequently all the three queens gave birth to sons. Kaushalya gave birth to Rama, after which Bharata was born to Kaikeyi and later on Sumitra gave birth to Lakshmana and Shatrughna. King Dasharatha was very happy and so were the people of Ayodhya. With great joy, they celebrated the birth of the four princes. Dasharatha loved all his sons but Rama was his dearest. He was very fond of his handsome, eldest son and could not bear to be away from him even for a moment.

# THE VALIANT PRINCES

The four princes grew up to be strong and handsome. Under sage Vashishta's guidance, they excelled themselves in archery, riding and hunting. They also learnt about the holy books and how to look after the welfare of the people. They respected their Gurus and the elders and gained the love and affection of people of Ayodhya. The brothers loved each other very much. Lakshmana was a very close companion to Rama. Bharata and Shatrughna were the other two inseparables.

King Dasharatha was very proud of his sons. One day he was discussing with sage Vashishta about finding suitable brides for his sons. At that time a great sage called Vishwamitra came to the court of Dasharatha. The king was very happy to welcome him to Ayodhya. After extending a warm hospitality, he asked Vishwamitra, "O great sage! Your visit has made me very happy. Pray, tell me the purpose of your visit. I shall deem it a great honour to abide by your wish."

Vishwamitra, pleased with the king's words told him, "King Dasharatha! I am pleased with your hospitality. I have heard that you always keep up your word; that's why I am here. I am about to perform a Yagna, but two Rakshasas— Mareecha and Subahu, pour blood and throw human flesh into the fire pit and pollute the Yagna. I cannot cast any curse on them as I am involved in a sacred work. But I cannot perform the Yagna till these demons are killed. Rama, your son, is the only valiant person who can kill them. Hence, please send him with me for ten days. As soon as the Yagna is completed, I will send back Rama to Ayodhya."

When the aged king heard this request, he felt nervous about sending his young son to fight against the demons. "Respected Sage," he pleaded with Vishwamitra, "My dear son Rama is still very young. How can he fight against the Rakshasas? Instead of Rama, I will send my entire army to help you in conducting the Yagna. I cannot bear to be separated from Rama and hence please spare me this agony."

Vishwamitra was angry at Dasharatha's words. "O King, you are going back on your word. I do not want anybody except Rama." So saying, he decided to walk out of the court. At this juncture, Vashishta pacified him and told Dasharatha, "Do not hesitate to send Rama. It is not a difficult task for Vishwamitra to kill the Rakshasas because he himself is very powerful. He wants to take Rama with him so that your son can learn to fight the Rakshasas even at this young age. Do send Rama with him."

Without any more hesitation, King Dasharatha blessed Rama and also Lakshmana, who wanted to be with his brother, and sent them with Vishwamitra.

Vishwamitra and the two princes travelling barefoot, first crossed the river Sarayu and then the river Ganga. Rama and Lakshmana did not mind the hardship at all as this was their chance to learn about many things from Vishwamitra. After many days of travelling, they entered a thick forest where a Rakshasi called Taraka lived. She had terrorised all the sages in the forest and hence Vishwamitra instructed Rama to kill her. Rama drew out his arrow and aimed it at Taraka. The ugly looking demoness charged towards him but was killed by Rama's arrow. Vishwamitra was very pleased with Rama and gifted him many powerful weapons. Rama accepted them gracefully and learnt from Vishwamitra about their use.

The trio continued their journey and reached the spot where Vishwamitra was to perform the Yagna. The Rishis of the Ashram were happy to have Rama in their midst. The princes rested for the night and from the next morning, protected the Yagna against the Rakshasas. Everything went on smoothly till the last day.

On the last day of the Yagna, suddenly, pieces of flesh and blood fell into the sacred fire. When Rama looked up, he saw Mareecha and Subahu rushing towards the fire pit. A horde of Rakshasas followed them. Without a moment's delay, Rama drew out his arrows and killed Mareecha and Subahu. The weapons were so strong and powerful that Mareecha was thrown into the sea hundreds of miles away while Subahu was engulfed in a ball of fire. All the Rishis were relieved that these evil demons were destroyed by Rama and they joyously completed the Yagna. After conducting the Yagna, Vishwamitra and the other Rishis left for the city of Mithila. Rama and Lakshmana accompanied them.

Mithila was ruled by King Janaka, who was loved and respected for his goodness. He had a beautiful daughter by name Sita. Janaka had found her in a ploughed field and had brought her up as his own daughter. Sita was lovely and was also renowned for her strength of character. When she was of a marriageable age, Janaka announced that whoever could string the Siva Bow would wed her. This bow was not an ordinary bow—it was a very huge and powerful bow given by Lord Shiva himself. Sage Vishwamitra knew about this bow and had purposely thought of taking the young princes to Mithila.

On their way to Mithila, they halted at an Ashram where Gautama, a sage, had once lived. Gautama had a wife called Ahalya who was extremely beautiful. Indra, the King of the Heavens, desired her and in Gautama's absence, deceived her. The enraged Gautama cast a curse on Indra. He also cursed Ahalya, " May you turn into a stone. You will be rid of this curse only when Sri Rama touches you." So saying, Gautama had gone away to the Himalayas to observe penance.

Vishwamitra narrated Ahalya's tragic story to Rama and instructed him, "Ramachandra! Rescue Ahalya from this curse and give her a new life." Rama followed this advice and as soon as he touched the stone statue, Ahalya came to life. At that moment Gautama also returned to the ashram. Thus, Gautama and Ahalya were re-united.

## SITA'S SWAYAMVAR

Vishwamitra, Rama and Lakshmana reached Mithila in time for Sita's Swayamvar. As per Janaka's wish, the mighty Siva Bow was hauled to the wedding hall. The hall wore a grand look and was occupied by many kings and princes. Ravana, the king of Lanka was also present and was confident that he could win Sita's hand easily. For, Janaka had announced that to win Sita's hand in marriage, any king or prince had to lift the bow and string it. Many tried, but failed. Even Ravana fell down while trying to lift the bow and had hurriedly disappeared from the hall out of shame. Vishwamitra turned towards Rama and told him gently, "Son! I am sure you are keen to examine the bow. Why don't you lift it and see how heavy it is?"

King Janaka was quite doubtful whether a young man like Rama would be able to achieve while the other well known kings and princes had failed. But he felt very impressed by Rama's noble looks and hence allowed him to contest.

Rama bowed before Vishwamitra to seek his blessings and walked up to the mighty Siva Bow. He lifted it up effortlessly and stringed it. The entire hall echoed with the sound of the bow being stringed. Except for Rama, Lakshmana and Vishwamitra, everybody else turned pale. Rama lifted the bow like a toy and broke it into two. King Janaka was extremely happy that Rama, the eldest prince of Ayodhya was to wed his daughter Sita.

On Vishwamitra's advice, Janaka sent messengers to Ayodhya to convey this happy news to Dasharatha. The message read: *Sri Rama has won the hand of my daughter Sita in swayamvar. I am inviting you and your family to come to Mithila and accept Sita as your daughter-in-law.*

King Dasharatha was delighted to hear this news and reached Mithila along with his wives, his ministers, sage Vashishta and others, to take part in the wedding.

While Rama wed Sita, Urmila married Lakshmana and Janaka's nieces, Mandavi and Shrutakirthi married Bharata and Shatrugna respectively.

These weddings were performed on a very grand scale. Dasharatha donated cows in the name of each of his sons, and not to be outdone, king Janaka made cash presents to all the brahmins. A grand feast was arranged for all the citizens. The newly wed couples were blessed by one and all.

Sita was a devout wife who always stood by her husband. The extremely beautiful Sita and the handsome Rama made an ideal couple.

The day after the wedding, Vishwamitra returned to his Ashram (hermitage). Dasharatha with his sons and daughters-in-law, along with his entourage left for Ayodhya. Halfway through their journey, a severe storm broke out. The entire atmosphere was filled with dust and was enveloped in darkness. At that time, a Rishi by name Parashurama appeared before them. His face was full of rage. He carried an axe on his shoulder and had an enormous bow with him. His awesome appearance proclaimed that he was no ordinary Rishi. He was the mighty

Parashurama who had conquered several Kshatriyas and had voyaged round the earth twenty-one times.

Parashurama went straight to Rama, and said in a sarcastic voice, "Rama, I heard that breaking the Siva Bow was very easy for you. I have a bigger and a mightier bow. Let us see whether you can string it." Dasharatha who was watching Parashurama, came running to him and prayed to him, "Parashurama, please calm down. My children have not done any harm to you. Bless them and spare Rama." Parashurama ignored Dasharatha's plea. He taunted Rama again and again.

Smiling gently, Rama picked up the bow very easily and fixed the arrow to it. He then asked Parashurama, "Sir, you are a brahmin and it would be improper for me to use the arrow on you. Hence, please tell me, what do I aim the arrow at?" Parashurama was stunned with Rama's mastery over the weapon. He could not say anything, but only gazed at Rama. It dawned upon him that Rama was no ordinary person but was an Avathar (reincarnation) of Lord Vishnu like himself born for a specific purpose. He then departed for the Himalayas to continue his penance.

King Dasharatha felt relieved, and the journey continued.

At Ayodhya, a grand reception awaited the newly-weds. For many days, this happy event was celebrated with pomp and pageantry. Dasharatha was very happy that his sons, especially Rama, were loved so much by the citizens of Ayodhya.

# KAIKEYI AND HER WISHES

Soon after Rama's, marriage with Sita, King Dasharatha wanted to crown him the king as he himself was getting older. Dasharatha therefore consulted his ministers about this. All of them whole-heartedly welcomed his decision. Dasharatha felt very happy and enthusiastic. He looked forward to the Coronation of Rama. He therefore immediately made announcements to this effect. He invited all the important people of Ayodhya and told them, "I have decided to crown my eldest son Rama. This is my ardent desire. If all of you agree, I will go ahead with the arrangements." Everybody was delighted. The people of Ayodhya rejoiced that Rama was to be their king.

Hectic preparations were on. Singers, dancers and other artistes were invited to the city to provide entertainment to the people. While these preparations were going on, Dasharatha had a talk with Rama and advised him about how a king should conduct himself, "A king should never fall a prey to vices. He should treat each and everyone with respect and rule the kingdom well." He also talked to his son about the duties of a king.

Kaushalya was very happy to hear that Rama was to be crowned shortly. She generously gifted valuable jewellery to those who conveyed this good news to her.

At the time of proclaiming that Rama was to be crowned, Bharata and Shatrugna, were away from Ayodhya. Sumitra, Shatrugna's mother, was also happy to hear the news.

When this news reached Kaikeyi, she was delighted that Rama was to be the king. But soon, Manthara, her maid, poisoned her mind.

"Queen Kaikeyi, have you forgotten that you also have a son? Your son Bharata has equal rights over this kingdom. If Rama becomes the king, then Kaushalya's haughtiness will know no bounds. You will be her maid and Bharata will be treated like Rama's servant. You are supposed to be king Dasharatha's favourite. But how has he proved it? By making Rama the king and by ignoring Bharata totally? Is it fair? Just think about the future."

"Why should I think about the future?" replied Kaikeyi, "Manthara, Rama is the eldest born. He is virtuous, he is valiant and is thoroughly well-versed in all sciences and arts. People love him. To tell you the truth, I love him more than my own son."

Manthara would not give up. Speaking in a loving tone, she told Kaikeyi, "Dear child! I am old enough to know the ways of the world. I can only pity you for your misplaced love towards Rama. Just imagine! What will be the fate of Bharata? And the king has taken this decision at a time when Bharata and Shatrugna are away from Ayodhya. The king knows that Lakshmana will be a mere puppet in his hands. Kaikeyi! Don't be idiotic. If you do not act now, you will be sending Bharata to exile."

Provoked by Manthara, Kaikeyi thought about what she said. She did not mind Rama being the king. But could she, the favourite wife of Dasharatha, be a slave to Kaushalya? "Never", she thought. So she immediately said to Manthara, "I agree with you. But how do we prevent Rama from becoming the king?"

"Simple," answered Manthara, "send him to the forest."

"But how?"

"Don't you remember that Dasharatha had agreed to grant you two wishes when you saved him in the war against Asuras? Ask them now. Dasharatha will come to your chambers to talk about Rama's Coronation. Show him that you are angry and demand your two wishes. First of all, demand that Bharata should be crowned the king. Your second wish should be to banish Rama to the forest for fourteen years."

Kaikeyi was totally changed. She forgot about Rama's love for her or that she had looked upon him as her own son. At that moment, Rama appeared to be her enemy, someone who was usurping Bharata of the kingdom. Filled with hatred and anger, she tore up all the fine clothes she had worn, she pulled out the jewellery and threw them on the floor. She sat huddled in a corner, thinking about Bharata's future and her misconstrued fears of becoming a slave to Kaushalya.

King Dasharatha came to Kaikeyi's chamber to share his happiness and to tell her about the grand preparations for the Coronation. But he was upset when he saw the strewn jewellery and the torn clothes. And when he saw his dear queen in tears, he was puzzled. He gently wiped her tears and asked her, "O, my precious one! Why are you angry? I will do anything to make you happy. I love you very dearly. Tell me, why are you so upset?" Kaikeyi grabbed this opportunity. "Will you grant me the two wishes due to me long ago?" she asked.

"Have no doubt, dear," said the king. "I swear on Rama that I will keep up my word."

Feeling bold, Kaikeyi demanded, "My first wish is that Bharata should be crowned the king. To fulfill my second wish, Rama should live in the forest like a hermit for fourteen years. Grant me these wishes right now. Otherwise, I will end my life."

King Dasharatha could not believe his own ears. He was horrified that Kaikeyi could be so mean and ruthless. "Are you playing a joke on me," he asked her.

"No, I am very serious," Kaikeyi said, laughing cruelly. The king was shocked. He fainted. After a while, he regained his consciousness and pleaded with her, "Kaika, give up these wishes. What you ask for is totally unfair. You have always told me that you love Rama as your son. Bharata has been very devoted to Rama and when he comes to know of your treachery, he will never forgive you. Don't Kaika, don't! Give up such dangerous thoughts. I cannot bear to be separated from Rama. Don't inflict this agony upon me in my old age. If you insist, I will crown Bharata as the king but please do not banish my Rama to the forest." King Dasharatha just could not control his emotions and wept bitterly.

Kaikeyi was unmoved. She did not want Rama in Ayodhya because she felt only then would Bharata gain the love and respect of the people of Ayodhya. So she was adamant. "Keep up your word," she insisted. The king went pale with anxiety. Rama was born as a result of the Yagna and that too, after being childless for a very long time. How could Dasharatha betray such a precious son. Why was Kaikeyi behaving in such a wicked manner? Who provoked her into this?

Tormented with these thoughts, the king again tried to change Kaikeyi's mind, "Kaika, are you angry that I decided on Rama's Coronation without telling you? If so, please forgive me. I beg of you. Agree to this

Coronation. People will love and respect you for this."

Kaikeyi did not budge. Dasharatha spent that night in Kaikeyi's chamber, pleading with her, begging her and crying for mercy. The Coronation was to take place the next morning.

The morning dawned. The city of Ayodhya wore a gay look. People were getting ready to take part in the Coronation ceremony. Vashishta and other sages were busy with rituals. Sumanthra, the minister, who was told that the king was in Kaikeyi's chambers, reached the room, only to find the king in a sad state. Kaikeyi stopped him from talking to the king and ordered him, "Sumanthra, go and fetch Rama here. I want to talk to him."

Sumanthra conveyed this message

to Rama and Rama reached Kalkeyi's chambers immediately. On seeing him, the old king just could not control his tears and cried out, "Rama! My dearest son, Rama!"

"Mother, why is father looking so pale and grief-stricken? Have I caused

him any anguish?" asked Rama politely.

Kaikeyi told him about her two wishes and about the king's reluctance to agree to them.

Without any hesitation, Rama agreed to carry out her wishes. "Mother, you want me to live in the forest like a hermit. Is that all? I will do anything for you. I will leave today itself. Bharata is my brother. I will be the happiest person to see him as the king. I will sacrifice even my life for him." Rama continued and said in a very calm voice, "For such a minor matter, I do not want to see my dear father unhappy. Please console him and please summon Bharata to Ayodhya at once."

Kaikeyi was delighted that Rama had agreed to carry out her wishes. "Rama, I will send word to Bharata.

Meanwhile, you can leave Ayodhya," she said.

On hearing this, Dasharatha cried out once again, "Kaika, Kaika, don't be so cruel." He could not even stand up properly.

Rama hurried to his father and hugging him lovingly, told him, "Dear father, it is my duty to honour any promise you have made." He turned towards Kaikeyi, "Mother, please allow me a few moments to tell my own mother and my wife Sita." He touched his parents' feet in salutation and left the chambers in a dignified manner.

Kaushalya on hearing the news, lamented, "Rama, my child! How can I live without you. Take me along with you to the forest." Lakshmana who heard this was enraged. "Why is father banishing Rama to the forest?

Is he afraid of Bharata? In that case, I will wipe out Bharata and his supporters," he shouted in anger. But Rama spoke in a calm and firm voice that it was his duty to carry out his father's promises. Kaushalya felt very sad. Should a prince like Rama live in a forest eating simple food and sleeping on a rough-straw mat? But Rama would not hear of any such argument and so, with a heavy heart, she bid farewell to her dearest son.

After taking leave of his mother, Rama went to talk to Sita. As soon as she heard that Bharata was to be the king and that Rama was to live in the forest, she decided to go with her husband. Rama tried to stop her and said, "Janaki, don't worry about me. Please stay back in the palace and take care of my mothers. Treat my brothers well. At the end of the fourteen year period, I will return safely to Ayodhya. No harm will come to me."

Sita replied, "Lord, I will follow you like a shadow. I do not want the comforts of the palace. Nothing can give me greater happiness than being with you." Rama tried his utmost to dissuade her. He said, "Wild beasts roam around in the forest. You will not have a soft bed to sleep on. Nor will there be good food to eat. Your tender feet will hurt when you walk on the thorny stretches of the forest."

Sita did not lose courage. "Aryaputra, how can the beasts attack me when you are there? Without you, even the softest bed will be like a bed of thorns. It is my duty to be with you. Please let me come with you," pleaded Sita. So Rama agreed to Sita's request.

Lakshmana who heard about Sita's decision, came running to Rama and fell at his feet and begged of him, "Please do not leave me behind. I will also come with you to the forest. Ayodhya will be like hell to me without you." Rama hesitated, for, there was a very strong bond of love and affection between the two of them. But at the same time, why should Lakshmana undergo such an exile for the sake of brotherly love, thought Rama. So he said, "Sowmithri, if you come away with me, who will, protect and look after our parents?" Lakshmana said, "Bharata will look after our parents. Whereas, you will have none with you in the forest. I can fetch you fruits and water and look after you and my respected sister-in-law." So saying, he went to his mother to break the news to her.

Sita, Rama and Lakshmana discarded all their royal clothes and wore rough saffron clothes. All that Rama and Lakshmana carried with them were their bows and arrows. By that time, this sad news had spread like wildfire all over Ayodhya and people wept at the thought that Rama, would not be their king. None could witness the scene of Rama, Sita and Lakshmana walking barefoot, dressed like hermits. "Fate is so cruel" thought many. "Will these three be able to face the dangers of a forest" was their only worry.

As Rama, Sita and Lakshmana entered Dasharatha's chamber to bid their final farewell to him, Dasharatha just could not control his anguish. "Rama, my dearest son, I wish I was robbed of my eyesight than to witness such a cruel scene. Will you ever forgive me, my son?" said

Dasharatha. Rama wiped his father's tears softly and said, "Father, I am duty bound to fulfill your wish. Please bless us."

Dasharatha realised that he could not make Kaikeyi change her mind nor could he make Rama go back on what he had said. In a trembling voice, he asked Sumanthra, the minister, to send the troops and servants along with Rama to the forest. This made Kaikeyi all the more angry. "O King! Is it fair on your part to send the troops away. Do you want my son to rule over an empty Ayodhya? No, no one should go with Rama," she said in a decisive tone.

Utterly defeated, Dasharatha ordered that Rama, Sita and Lakshmana be taken by chariot at least till the outskirts of Ayodhya. "I cannot bear to see them walking through the streets of Ayodhya," he said. Since Kaikeyi did not object to this, Sumanthra got a chariot readied.

Sri Rama, Sita and Lakshmana touched the feet of all their elders to seek their blessings. As Rama, Sita and Lakshmana got into the chariot, the entire population of Ayodhya wept. 'How could the king behave so foolishly" ridiculed some. Will the old parents bear the separation from their dear son, they thought.

The chariot started moving. King Dasharatha wanted to have a last look at Rama. Seeing this, Rama wanted the chariot to move faster, but the old king ran behind it crying out, "Rama! Rama!" Kaushalya also followed the chariot. People averted their eyes, as they could not withstand such a pitiable scene. Rama's eyes were filled with tears. As the chariot moved faster, Dasharatha collapsed on the street. When Kaikeyi tried to help him, he cried, "Don't ever touch me. I don't want to see you again. Just go away."

Even when the chariot began to move faster, people followed it. Rama again appealed to them, "I know of your enormous love and affection for me. From now on, Bharata will be your king. Please show him the same love and affection that you have for me." The citizens insisted that they would follow him to the forest. By that time, the chariot had reached the Tamasa river bank. Since they ran behind the chariot for a long distance, they were all tired and soon fell asleep under the trees. Taking advantage of this, Rama ordered Sumanthra to take him to the borders of Kosala country. Before dawn, Rama, Sita and

Lakshmana reached the banks of the river Ganga.

When the citizens woke up in the morning, they realised that Rama, Sita and Lakshmana were nowhere in the vicinity. They had no other option than to return to Ayodhya.

Rama decided to cross the Ganga and continue their journey. In the nearby forest lived Guha, the king of the hunters. As he was a friend of Rama, he was very happy to see him. Welcoming Rama, Sita and Lakshmana, Guha offered them many delicacies to eat. But Rama refused these saying that since his exile had begun, he would only eat simple food. He stayed there overnight and slept on the hard floor. He was very worried about his father. So, the next morning, he requested Sumanthra to return to Ayodhya and to take care of his parents. Sumanthra reluctantly agreed to return to Ayodhya. The three travellers bid good-bye to Guha and walked through the dense jungle. Lakshmana walked in front, clearing the jungle path, Sita walked in-between and Rama walked behind her. It was not easy for them to walk bare-foot on the thorny paths. But they walked on cheerfully, admiring the way huge trees grew, how the insects collected their food and so on. In the night, they slept on the grassy slopes of a hill and at dawn, started their journey again. On the way, they halted at the hermitage of Bharadwaj. Sage Bharadwaj' was delighted with his guests and extended a warm hospitality to them. He then suggested that they live in Chitrakut region, which was full of enchanting scenery.

Rama, Sita and Lakshmana, followed his advice and reached Chitrakut by crossing the river Yamuna.

Rama liked the place very much. So, he decided to live there and asked Lakshmana to set up Parnakuti, a thatched hut. Rama performed rituals and offered prayers to his elders and entered his new home. Malyavati river flowed nearby. Flowering trees and fruit trees were found to be in plenty. Beautiful butterflies and the sweet singing of the birds lent an enchantment. Sita loved the place very much.

In the meantime, Sumanthra had returned to Ayodhya. By then, he had received news about Rama, Sita and Lakshmana having reached Chitrakut. Without Rama's presence, the entire Ayodhya looked like a ghost city. People seemed disinterested in everything. And when they saw Sumanthra return in an empty chariot, they wept.

Sumanthra's return to Ayodhya kindled a small hope in Dasharatha. May be Rama was persuaded to give up his word and return to the kingdom, he thought. "I do not want to live without my Rama," he cried. He could only think of Rama's birth, his childhood and his marriage to Sita. "I have lost such a wonderful son. I do not know what sin I committed." Then, he suddenly remembered an incident which occurred when he was young.

Dasharatha had once gone hunting and had reached Sarayu river. It was a dark night and he heard a sound of splashing water. He thought that a wild beast had come to drink water and aimed his arrow in the direction from which the sound came. When Dasharatha tried to trace his game, he found that his arrow had pierced a young lad by name Sravanakumar. This boy was fetching water for his blind parents. Dasharatha at once picked him in his arms. But by the time he took him to his blind parents, the boy was already dead. The grief-stricken father of Sravanakumar cursed Dasharatha, "O King! You have killed my son and thus separated me from him. This grief will cause me my death. You shall also die, pining for your son."

Dasharatha told Kaushalya about this incident and holding her hands, said, "The sage's curse has come true now. Please forgive me for all my sins." The king recalled each and every feature of the handsome Rama and with tears blurring his eyes, and cried out, "I wanted my son to be near me when I died. Kaikeyi has destroyed even this. She is my true enemy. Kaushalya! Sumitra! I do not want to live any longer. My eyes are failing. Rama, my son! Rama, my son!" uttering these words, the king died.

Ayodhya which was still grieving over Rama's exile, was plunged into sorrow as the news of the king's death spread. "But what a tragedy? The king who had four mighty sons, died when none of them was near him. Who will perform his funeral rites" debated the people. Sage Vashishta therefore made arrangements for the body to be preserved for a longer time.

Dasharatha's ministers hurriedly called a meeting and on Vashista's advice, sent word to Bharata who had gone to visit his maternal relatives.

The messengers were instructed not to disclose to Bharata about Rama's exile and the king's death. On receiving the message, Bharata immediately hurried back to Ayodhya. Just the previous night, he had some evil omens and he was anxious to return home at the earliest.

On reaching Ayodhya, Bharata was shocked to see people huddled in corners and weeping. No prayers were offered. No chanting of Vedas could be heard. Not even one child was found playing in the streets. There was a deathly silence everywhere. The worried Bharata first went to his father's chamber, but found it empty. So he went to Kaikeyi's chambers hoping to find his father there, but only Kaikeyi was there. "Mother, where is Father? What has happened in my absence?" he asked.

Kaikeyi thought that Bharata would be very pleased to hear that she had got him the kingdom of Ayodhya. In a gentle tone, she said, "Son! Nobody can prevent death. Your father has passed away." Shocked by this news, Bharata collapsed. The death of his father, whom he loved so dearly, brought tears to his eyes. "I wish I was with my father when he died," he thought. "Atleast Rama and Lakshmana have had that great honour," he said aloud. "Mother, I shall go and see Rama and find out if my father had any last message for me."

Kaikeyi stopped him from leaving and said, "Son, wait. Your father cried out only for Rama, Sita and Lakshmana. He said he could not live without them." Bharata felt that there was more bad news.

"Why, mother? Isn't Rama in Ayodhya? Where has he gone?" he asked.

Kaikeyi then had to tell him everything. Placing her hand over his head, she said, "Bharata, your brother Rama along with Sita and Lakshmana are now living in a forest. I have got you the kingdom of Ayodhya."

Bharata was stunned to hear this. Feeling enraged, he told his mother, "I am ashamed to call you my mother. You are nothing but evil. How could you banish Rama to the forest? Hadn't you loved him more than you loved me? Alas! You have killed my father, just to make me the king. And do you expect me to wear the crown that rightfully belongs to Rama? Shame on you!"

Full of scorn and anger towards his mother, Bharata decided to atone for her sins. "I will go to the forest and live there for the rest of my life. But before that, I will bring back Rama and make him the king."

He then went to Kaushalya and sobbing bitterly, he fell at her feet and said, "Mother, I am the sinner. I have been the cause of my father's death and my brother's exile to the forest. Will you ever forgive me and my own mother?" Kaushalya consoled him that none can change the course of destiny. She knew of his pure mind.

Bharata met the ministers. He offered his salutations to Sage Vashishta. On seeing Bharata, Vashishta made arrangements for the funeral of Dasharatha. With a heavy heart, Bharata performed all the rites a son ought to do.

Shatrugna wanted to punish Manthara for her evil thoughts and for provoking Kaikeyi. But Bharata did not want to subject an old woman to cruel treatment and so, she was pardoned.

Bharata lost interest in everything. For hours, he sat alone and in shame and anger, thinking about his father's death and about Rama. He refused to be crowned as the king. "In Raghu dynasty, none has witnessed a younger son becoming the king. I will bring back Rama and go to the forest in his place," he vowed.

So, the next day, Bharata left Ayodhya with a large army. The people of Ayodhya followed him. The queens including Kaikeyi went with them. By that time Kaikeyi realised that she had committed a grave mistake. She was very repentant and wanted to plead with Rama to forgive her.

When this huge group of soldiers and people reached the area where Guha lived, Guha at first thought that Bharata had brought his army to kill Rama and retain the kingdom even after the period of fourteen years. So, he asked Bharata, "Why have you brought such a huge army? If you plan to attack Rama, you will have to defeat me first."

Bharata was extremely hurt by this suspicion. But he explained to Guha that he would take Rama back to Ayodhya and crown him the king. Guha was very happy to hear this. So he helped Bharata, his army and his retinue to cross the Ganga.

As Bharata and his army approached Chitrakut, Lakshmana saw them coming, and at once informed Rama, "Brother, take up your bow. Bharata is coming here

with a big army to kill you. His
mother banished you to the forest. He
will not hesitate to kill you. I will fight
against him and kill him," he said
angrily.

Rama listened to Lakshmana
calmly and said, "Lakshmana, you
have misunderstood Bharata. He
probably has come here to ask me to
return to Ayodhya. Don't talk hastily.
Don't talk ill of Bharata." Lakshmana
never disobeyed his brother. So he
kept quiet. As soon as Bharata saw
Rama, he ran towards him and fell at
his feet. Rama embraced his brother
and was concerned to see agony on his
face. So he asked Bharata, "How is
father? Have you taken over the
affairs of the kingdom?" Bharata could
not control himself any longer and
sobbing he said, "Our father died
heart-broken. He could not bear the
grief of your exile."

On hearing this news, tears welled up in Rama's eyes. "Bharata, how unfortunate I am! I could not look after my father even when he was dying. Nor did I have the opportunity to perform my father's last rites." Sita and Lakshmana too were shell-shocked to hear about king Dasharatha's death.

Bharata who had come dressed in the clothes of a hermit, told his brother, "Rama, please return to Ayodhya and rule over it. Instead of you, I will stay back in the forest." Rama was deeply moved by Bharata's love for him. But he said in a firm voice, "No, Bharata, I am here to fulfill my father's promise. You should also respect his wishes. We should not disobey our father. I will rule over Ayodhya only after completing my exile in the forest."

Bharata tried his level best to make Rama change his mind. The sages also tried to influence Rama, but in vain. Rama's only answer was, "It is my duty to carry out the wishes of my parents."

Bharata made one more attempt to persuade Rama. "I do not have the capability to rule over the kingdom. Come back to Ayodhya at least for my sake," he pleaded. Rama smiled gently at him and said, "Bharata, you are a very intelligent and capable person. You have the expert knowledge of your ministers with you. And the responsibility of ruling over Ayodhya is yours. Go back and rule over it well."

With no other option, Bharata said, "Brother, I will rule over Ayodhya on your behalf. So please give me your sandals. I will place them on the throne." Rama agreed to this.

Speaking again, Bharata swore, "I hereby take an oath that I shall await your return and for this period of fourteen years I shall not wear any royal clothes and I shall subsist only on fruits and tubers. If you do not return on the appointed day, I will jump into the fire and end my life."

Such was the love between the two brothers. Rama hugged his brother and advised him, "Please treat our mother Kaikeyi well. Be happy. Be kind to others."

Bharata placed his brother's sandals over his head and carried them to Ayodhya. He did not like to live in Ayodhya without Rama. So he chose a small village called Nandigram near Ayodhya. He placed the padukas (sandals) on the throne and coronated them. "I am merely a servant of my brother," he announced. "These padukas are the true masters," he said. He showed due respect to these padukas and remembering Rama at each and every step, ruled over Ayodhya. People felt safe and happy under him.

Sri Rama wanted to go away from Chitrakut as the place reminded him of Bharata and his mothers. So he decided to leave the area and move on. The three of them wandered through dense forests, leading a peaceful, contented life.

# THE DEMONS IN THE FORESTS

Many of these forests had sages living in them. Many more had demons in them, destroying everything and at times even disrupting the lives of the sages. Dandakaranya was one such forest.

When Rama, Sita and Lakshmana entered this forest, the Rishis welcomed them, offered them fruits and nuts. A thatched hut was specially erected for them. Happy and contented, Rama decided to spend the night there.

All of a sudden, a very ugly creature appeared before him. It had the body of a demon with huge, bulging eyes and a big mouth. It's stomach was a big mound. This demon was Viradha. He had a Trishul in one hand with which he used to pierce and carry animals. Viradha was a terror to the Rishis. He had been granted a boon by Brahma that no weapon would kill him.

As soon as Viradha saw the beautiful Sita, he grabbed her and wanted to marry her. Enraged, Rama used a sharp arrow on him. Though the arrow was powerful it could not kill Viradha, but only caused him severe injuries. Viradha put down Sita and fought with Rama. Rama and Lakshmana used their weapons and injured Viradha's body. Viradha could not be defeated. Soon he tucked Rama and Lakshmana under his arms and started running. At once Rama and Lakshmana chopped off his arms.

Viradha fell to the ground. Lakshmana broke all his bones. Still he did not die. Finally, Rama and Lakshmana dug a pit and buried Viradha. They covered the pit with huge boulders.

Rama, Sita and Lakshmana continued their journey through the forest and reached Panchavati. It was a lovely spot and Sita liked it very much. So, on Rama's instructions, Lakshmana built a hut. Nearby flowed the river Godhavari. Flowers bloomed everywhere and their fragrance filled the air. The three of them lived peacefully there.

One day a demoness by name Surpanakha passed by. She saw Rama and Lakshmana talking to each other. The handsome Rama caught her attention and she fell in love with him. Surpanakha was ugly and hideous. She had rough, red hair. Her body was massive with a huge tummy. Her eyes were red and evil looking. Her voice was so powerful that the whole forest seemed to vibrate whenever she opened her mouth.

She went straight to Rama and asked him, "Who are you?" Rama replied that he was the son of Dasharatha and he then asked her who she was.

Laughing hoarsely, she said, "I am Surpanakha. I am the only sister of king Ravana of Lanka. Kumbakarna and Vibhishana are my brothers. The mighty Khara and Dushana are also my brothers. Rama, I am desirous of you. I have never seen anyone so handsome. Marry me. Be my husband." She paused for a moment and said, "Please don't think I am ugly.

I can turn myself into a beautiful girl. I can make you very happy."

Rama smiled and replied, "Surpanakha, I am already married. Do you see the beautiful lady over there? She is my wife Sita. As I told you earlier, this is my brother Lakshmana. He is also married but has left his wife behind. I suggest you propose to him."

Surpanakha thought it to be a good idea and went to Lakshmana and said, "O Lakshmana, did you hear about what your brother said? Come, let us get married and lead a happy life." Lakshmana said jokingly, "My dear lady, I am a humble servant of Rama. If you marry me, you will have to be a maid here. Rama will be a king in a few years. It's best if you marry him. You can then be the queen."

Surpanakha pestered Rama again,

"Rama, marry me. Otherwise I will gobble up Sita and then force you to marry me." Rama refused. The angry Surpanakha tried to attack Sita, but Lakshmana quickly drew out his sword and cut off her ears and nose.

Screaming with pain and rage,

Surpanakha ran to her brother Khara and told him about how Rama and Lakshmana ill-treated her. "I want to drink Sita's blood. I also want the severed heads of Rama and Lakshmana. My dear brother, please fulfill my wish," she said.

Khara, who was infuriated on seeing the condition of his dear sister, ordered fourteen of his fellow-demons to kill Rama and Lakshmana. But Rama knocked them down. Within moments, all of them were dead.

Khara then took a large army of Rakshasas with him and promised his sister that he would gift her Rama's head. Each of the Rakshasas of the army charged menacingly towards Rama. Rama fought against them single-handed while Lakshmana stood guard near Sita. Rama destroyed the entire army and soon killed Khara and

Dushana also. The Rishis and the Suras who were watching this battle showered petals on Rama and hailed his victory over the demons. They were grateful to Rama for bringing peace to Dandakaranya.

Sita and Lakshmana were very happy that Rama fought valiantly against the powerful Khara and Dushana.

Surpanakha who also witnessed the mighty power of Rama fled to Lanka. When she reached the court of Ravana, he was conducting a meeting with his ministers about an important matter relating to Lanka. Surpanakha entered the court in a dramatic way, crying loudly and trying to cover her gaping nose with her hand. Ravana was horrified to see his sister in such a condition. Even before he could say anything,

Surpanaka burst out, "Ravana, my brother! All the Rakshasas have been killed. Khara and Dushana are dead. And imagine! Just one human being is responsible for all this disaster. A man by name Rama has killed fourteen thousand Rakshasas and also Khara and Dushana. Rama is not ordinary person. When he uses his arrows, it appears as though there is a rain of arrows. And here you are leading a life of luxury, not caring, about your brothers who died at the hands of Rama."

"But dear sister, who caused you all these injuries and why?" asked, Ravana.

"Dear brother, Rama has a very lovely wife called Sita. I wanted to bring her to you as a gift. Rama got angry and ordered his brother Lakshmana to chop off my nose and ears," lied Surpanakha.

"Just to please me, you faced such danger, is it?" asked Ravana.

"Yes, even our brothers Khara and Dushana and a great number of Rakshasas sacrificed their lives to bring you the lovely Sita."

Surpanakha continued to provoke Ravana's anger, "Brother, you are so strong and mighty. Kidnap Sita and keep her with you. Only then can you take revenge against Rama for his misdeeds."

Ravana, who had attended Sita's Swayamvar, had not forgotten her immense beauty. Nor had he forgotten how Rama had won her hand by humiliating all the other kings and princes. His wicked mind urged him not to lose this chance to take revenge. So he thought of a plan to kidnap Sita.

The next morning Ravana flew in his Pushpak Viman and reached the home of Maricha, Taraka's son. He described to Maricha the way in which Surpanakha was disfigured and how Khara and Dushana met a cruel death. "I have to take revenge against Rama. Only then will my brothers find peace in heaven. That's why I want to separate Sita and Rama," said Ravana.

Maricha who had earlier faced Rama's arrows, trembled with fear just at the mention of his name. "Ravana, you are ill-advised. Carrying away Sita is to carry death with you. Sita is another man's wife. Give up such wicked thoughts and go back to Lanka," advised Maricha.

Ravana would not listen to Maricha. He insisted on Maricha's help and then explained his plan, "Maricha, if you are so afraid of Rama's arrows, you need not face him at all.

You have magical powers and can turn yourself into any other form. All that I ask of you is to turn yourself into a beautiful golden deer and roam in front of Sita's hut. Sita will definitely want you. So she will ask Rama and Lakshmana to catch you. When they try to chase you, you can run fast and take them away from Panchavati. With none to protect her, Sita can be easily kidnapped. And unable to bear the separation, Rama will die."

Maricha once again told Ravana, "O king! You already have so many beautiful wives. Do not lust for Sita. She will be the cause of your death and destruction of Lanka."

"Ha... Ha...... laughed Ravana scornfully. "How can an ordinary man like Rama cause my death? I live beyond the ocean and he cannot even reach me there."

"I am warning you Maricha," he continued. "If you do not help me in this plan, I will kill you at this very spot." Maricha knew that either way he would be killed. He preferred to die at Rama's hands and so agreed to Ravana's plans. Ravana took him in his Pushpak Viman and dropped him near Panchavati.

# THE KIDNAPPING OF SITA

Maricha turned himself into a golden deer and roamed in front of Sita's hut when she came out to pluck flowers. Sita was enchanted to see such a beautiful creature and called out to Rama, "Can you please catch this exquisite creature for me? Let us take it to Ayodhya when we get back," she said.

Lakshmana who also saw the golden deer was cautious. So he told Rama, "Brother, somehow I feel that this is not a real animal. I feel that this is some Rakshasa in the guise of a deer."

Sri Rama had also taken a great liking for the deer and he brushed Lakshmana's advice aside.

"Lakshmana, this deer is rather unusual. I also like it as much a Janaki. If, as you say, it is really a Rakshasa I can kill it and get rid of the Rakshasa. Be careful. Look after

Sita till I return." So saying Rama went in pursuit of the animal.

Rama ran behind the deer and just as he was about to catch it, it ran faster and faster. Rama chased it on and on but he still could not catch it Tired and unable to catch it alive, Rama used his arrow. As soon as the arrow hit the deer, it fell down and its body turned once again into the body of a Rakshasa. Before dying, Maricha imitated Rama's voice and cried out, "Ah Sita! Ah Lakshmana!" Rama at once realised that this was a trick of the Rakshasa and fearing for the safety of Sita, hurried back to the Ashram.

When Maricha's cry reached Sita's ears, she felt scared and told Lakshmana, "Your brother is in danger. Please go to his rescue."

Lakshmana tried to calm her by

assuring that no harm could ever come to Rama. When she insisted that Lakshmana leave at once in search of Rama, Lakshmana refused. She got angry. "Lakshmana, didn't you hear what I said? Instead of going to Rama's help, you stand here like a stone statue. Are you Rama's enemy? Have you no concern for the safety of your brother?" she said. Lakshmana was hurt by Sita's words, but still he said calmly, "Rama is very valiant. No harm can come to him. As I told you earlier, the golden deer was probably Maricha. My brother Rama has instructed me not to leave you alone. I shall follow his orders." In her anxiety about Rama's safety, Sita accused Lakshmana of evil intentions and threatened to end her life if Lakshmana did not go to Rama's help.

Lakshmana was extremely hurt by Sita's accusations and so, decided to go in search of Rama. Before he went, he warned Sita to be careful, about strangers. He also drew a line just outside the door of the hut with his arrow and told her, "Respected sister-in-law! Please do not cross this line in any event. I will soon be back with Rama. May God protect you!"

Ravana who had hid behind a tree waiting for Sita to be left alone, turned himself into a poor Sanyasi and called out in front of the hut, "Alms for a poor Sanyasi!" Thinking that a hungry person was at the door, Sita opened it with the food vessel in her hand. Ravana found her even more beautiful than ever and this made him determined to have her at any cost.

Sita stood at the door, not wanting to cross the line Lakshmana had drawn in front of the hut. So, to make her cross the line, Ravana pretended to be very weak with hunger and said, "My lady, please hand over the alms to me here."

As soon as the unsuspecting Sita walked over and beyond the line, Ravana grabbed her hand and revealed his true identity. "O beautiful Sita, I am Ravana, the mighty king of Lanka. I have come here to take you to my kingdom. Forget about Rama, who cannot even feed you well in this forest. I will treat you like a queen and give you all the luxuries of life."

Sita was very angry at such indecent talk. She tried to pull away her hand. Ravana ignored her warnings and forcibly dragged her to his Pushpak Viman. Soon he was airborne. Sita, who was trembling like a fawn, cried out, "Rama, Rama, Lakshmana. Where are you? The

wicked Ravana is taking me away."
But there was no response. So, she
made a fervent plea to the trees and
the birds to convey the message to
Rama that she was in distress.
Jatayu, the king of birds, heard her
cries. As soon as she saw him, she
pleaded with Jatayu, "Will you please
tell Rama about my kidnapping and
save me from this wicked man."
Jatayu blocked Ravana's way and
advised him, "Leave Sita alone. A
king of your stature should not resort
to such a wicked act. Sita is another
man's wife. What would you have
done if your wife was kidnapped by
another man? Rama will certainly kill
you for this. But before that, I will
fight against you and rescue Sita."

Ravana laughed at Jatayu. "You are
nothing but a bird. Are you going to
rescue this beautiful lady?"

"I will show you my strength," challenged Jatayu. And then they fought with each other high up in the skies. Jatayu scratched and injured Ravana's body with his sharp claws. He was deeply touched by Sita's tears and her helpless condition. So, even at the cost of his own life, Jatayu fought with Ravana. With his powerful wings, he broke Ravana's bow. This made Ravana very angry and he chopped Jatayu's wings with his sword. He cut off the legs too. Jatayu lost the power to fly and fell on the ground. Sita was dismayed that Jatayu died for her sake. She plunged into immense sorrow. Then, the flight continued.

On the way, the helpless Sita cursed Ravana. "Wicked Ravana, you have invited death, for, my husband is not an ordinary man. He is the bravest among the brave. He is unrivalled in the art of warfare. He can kill you with a single arrow," threatened Sita. None of these words had any effect on Ravana. He was mighty pleased with himself that he was about to enjoy Sita's company.

Feeling desperate, Sita looked down and noticed a group of monkeymen sitting atop a hill. Without losing any more time, she removed all her ornaments, wrapped them in a portion of her upper garment and threw down the bundle so that it fell amidst the monkeymen. The surprised monkeymen looked up but by that time Ravana had zoomed past them. He crossed the ocean and reached Lanka.

Ravana kept Sita in his royal chamber and appointed Rakshasis to guard her. He instructed them to look after Sita well and not to hurt her.

Ravana thus hoped that Sita would eventually change her mind about him and agree to be his queen.

Ravana made it a habit to visit her everyday, carrying expensive gifts, with him. He pestered her, pleaded with her and tried all sorts of methods to make Sita agree to his desire.

Sita was disgusted by the way he talked. As soon as Ravana came to the chamber she would close her eyes and ears with her hands.

"Ravanasur, you are talking to me in an immoral way. Whatever you say or do, I won't even look at you or listen to you. You tricked me into believing that you are a Sanyasi. Alas! I did not listen to Lakshmana's advice," lamented Sita. Everyday she wept bitterly at her misfortune.

Irritated with her persistent refusals, Ravana warned her, "Sita, I will allow you one year's time. If by then, you do not change your mind and wed me, I shall cut you into pieces." He ordered the Rakshasis to guard Sita in Ashoka garden and to try to make her agree to his proposal.

# RAMA SEARCHES FOR SITA

When Lakshmana reached the spot where Maricha lay dead, both Rama and Lakshmana at once knew that Sita was in danger. So they hurried back to Panchavati but were shocked to find it empty. They searched and searched for her. Rama went to the Godavari bank but could not find her there.

Rama was heart-broken. Life seemed meaningless without Sita. With tears rolling down his cheeks, he recalled the way in which Sita would stroll in the garden, how happy she was in Panchavati and so on. At times, he turned his wrath on

Lakshmana for leaving Sita alone. Lakshmana tried to explain to Rama about how reluctant he was to leave Sita alone and about how Sita insisted that he go in search of Rama.

But this did not console Rama in any way. He roamed through the forests like a madman, calling out her name so often, talking to plants and animals about Sita. All their efforts to trace Sita were in vain. Rama and Lakshmana did not give up their efforts to find Sita. They kept on walking and suddenly they noticed Jatayu, who was wounded and was bleeding profusely. Rama at first thought that this was a Rakshasa in the form of a bird and drew out his arrow to kill Jatayu. Just then he heard Jatayu say in a feeble voice, "Rama, I am Jatayu. I tried to prevent Ravana from abducting Sita and just look at my condition! I am about to die any moment now. Sri Rama, are you going to kill me?"

Rama kept aside his weapons, picked up the bird in his arms and gently touched his body. Jatayu told Rama, "Rama! I tried my best to save Sita. Please kill Ravana, free Sita and lead a happy life." He died in Rama's arms, contented that he had the good fortune of rendering some service to Rama.

Rama performed Jatayu's last rites as a son would do for his father. Then Rama and Lakshmana continued their journey westwards.

On their way, they were stopped by a cruel looking Rakshasa. He had arms which were several miles long. With one sweep of the arm, this Rakshasa, whose name was Kabandha, lifted Rama and Lakshmana up in the air. He was about to gobble them up when both of them chopped off his arms. Screaming with pain, Kabandha wanted to know who they were. When Rama revealed his identity, Kabandha bowed before him and narrated his story.

Kabandha was once very handsome. But he would turn himself into a terrifying creature just to scare the Rishis and kill them. Once a Rishi cursed him, "May this hideous form stay! Only when Rama comes to this forest and chops your arms will you be able to regain your good-looks."

Kabandha got back his good looks and commanded a flying-machine to take him to heaven. Before departing, he wished Rama and Lakshmana well and said, "Rama, Sugriva is a monkey king who lives in the hills of Rishyamukha by the side of Pampa lake. Make him your friend. He will help you to know the whereabouts of Sita."

So the two brothers proceeded towards Rishyamukha. Tired and hungry, they walked on and in the midst of a forest, they noticed an Ashram. Sabari, a Sanyasini lived here. She was very old and could hardly see or walk. But still she had gathered nuts and fruits hoping to feed them to Rama. Hence when she saw Rama along with his brother at her doorsteps, her happiness knew no bounds. She extended her hospitality to them.

Sabari's love and devotion towards Rama earned her a place in heaven.

From Sabari's Ashram, Rama and Lakshmana reached the hills of Rishyamukha and rested for a while near Pampa lake.

# THE LAND OF THE MONKEYS

Even when Sri Rama tried to take some rest, he always pined for Sita. He could not eat, nor could he sleep. Lakshmana who sadly watched his brother's condition, tried to instil some hope and confidence in him. "Dear brother," he told Rama, "Please do not lose heart. I am sure we can trace Sita and free her from Ravana".

"Then, let us not waste any more time," said Rama and soon they reached Rishyamukha.

Rishyamukha was a hilly region where many Vanaras lived. Sugriva was their leader. He had the assistance and friendship of

Hanuman, a valiant and highly intelligent Vanara born with the blessings of gods.

Sugriva had an elder brother called Vali. Vali was the king of Kishkinda. The two brothers loved each other. Once Vali fought against a demon and chased him into a cave. Before entering he asked Sugriva to stand guard at its entrance. Sugriva waited there patiently, but Vali did not come out for many days. He was deeply worried. To add to his worry, he heard the demon roar and also saw blood flow out of the cave. He thought Vali was dead and closed the cave with a huge rock and returned to Kishkinda. Since the kingdom was without a king, people crowned Sugriva as the king.

One day all of a sudden Vali returned. When he came to know that

Sugriva had become the king, he was very angry. He banished Sugriva from the kingdom and even kept back Sugriva's wife.

Sugriva took shelter in Rishyamukha as Vali could not enter the area because of a curse.

When Rama and Lakshmana reached Rishyamukha, Sugriva at first thought that they had come on behalf of Vali to kill him. So he sent Hanuman to find out who they were.

Hanuman introduced himself to Rama and told him about Sugriva. In turn, Lakshmana told him about themselves and said, "O Vanara! A Rakshasa called Ravana has abducted my sister-in-law. We do not know where he lives. We are here to ask for Sugriva's help to know more about Ravana. We are not here to kill Sugriva."

Satisfied with this reply, Hanuman carried Rama and Lakshmana on his shoulders and with a powerful hop, reached the peak where Sugriva lived.

Sugriva, on hearing about Rama's plight, embraced him warmly and told him, "Rama, I will help you in your search for Sita. Wherever she is, we will find her. Oh Yes! Now I remember. A few days back, we saw a woman being abducted by a Rakshasa. We heard her cry, "Rama! Lakshmana! Please save me." She then threw down some of her ornaments tied in a piece of cloth. I will fetch these for you. Please see whether they belong to Mother Sita." So saying, Sugriva asked one of the Vanaras to fetch the ornaments.

As soon as Rama saw the ornaments, tears welled up in his eyes and crying out Sita's name, he fainted.

After a while he regained consciousness and asked Lakshmana, "Brother, please make sure that these belong to Sita." But Lakshmana could not identify any head ornament or ear ornament. He bowed his head and said, "I have never looked at my respected sister-in-law above her feet. I can only identify the articles on her feet as I have noticed them while touching her feet everyday." Such was the respect Lakshmana had towards his brother's wife.

Rama then looked at the ornaments once again and knew for certain that they belonged to his dearest wife. He swore, "I will kill Ravana who has separated Sita from me."

Sugriva consoled his friend Rama and promised him that he would send the Vanara army to trace Sita and then help in killing Ravana. In return, the grateful Rama offered to kill Vali and help Sugriva in regaining his kingdom and his wife. Sugriva who was still not aware of Rama's' enormous skill and bravery was doubtful whether he could fight against the very powerful Vali.

"Dear friend," he told Rama, "I am glad with your offer to kill Vali. But I know my brother well. I have seen with my own eyes how Vali knocked down a line of seven trees with a single arrow. If you can also prove your skill, I will feel assured."

Upon this Rama felled seven trees in a line with a single arrow. This made Sugriva very happy. So he went to Kishkinda and challenged Vali to a duel. This angered Vali a lot and he accepted Sugriva's challenge at once. But in no time at all, Sugriva was overpowered by Vali. Just at that time, Rama, who was hiding behind a tree, shot an arrow capable of killing Vali. It hit him on the chest and Vali fell to the ground. Stunned by such an unexpected attack, Vali looked around and saw Rama. "Rama, is it fair on your part to hide behind a tree like a coward and kill me?" accused

Vali. He added "You are a righteous man. How could you stoop to such level? And moreover, what grudge do you bear against me? Am I your enemy? Answer me, Rama. Without any reason you have attacked me. What you have done is wrong."

In reply Rama said, "Vali, Sugriva is my friend. In fact, he is like a brother to me. You had forcibly kept back his wife. So I had to kill you. Moreover you are not a human being. You are a Vanara. So I am justified in killing you in a surprise attack."

Vali could not say anything against this argument. So, he took Sugriva's hand in his own and asked him to look after his own son Angada well. In a few moments Vali was dead.

Sugriva who regained the kingdom of Kishkinda, soon forgot all about helping Rama to trace Sita. Rama and

Lakshmana lived in a cave, waiting for Sugriva's help. Sugriva lived the life of a king, enjoying all the luxuries. This annoyed Lakshmana very much as he could no longer watch his brother pining for Sita. So he immediately rushed to Kishkinda swearing that he would kill Sugriva for breaking his promise. Alarmed at such anger, Hanuman hurried to Sugriva and reminded him about his promise to Rama. "Hasn't Rama proved his friendship to you? Shouldn't you repay his gratitude?" he asked.

Realising his mistake, Sugriva hastened to Rama and begged for forgiveness. He then ordered Hanuman to summon all the Vanaras to Kishkinda. Soon, thousands of Vanaras assembled at Kishkinda and Sugriva instructed them to search for Sita in all the four directions. He separately instructed Hanuman,

"Maruthi! You are the most capable of all the Vanaras. I am sure that you will bring us the good news very soon." Rama also agreed with Sugriva. He called Hanuman aside and gave him his ring. "When you meet Sita, please show her this ring. She will then know that you are truly my messenger" Hanuman accepted the ring with devotion and after touching Rama's feet in reverence, left on his mission.

Sugriva had given one month's time to the Vanaras to trace Sita. They searched and searched but just could not get any news about her. One group of Vanaras which had gone in the southern direction under Hanuman's leadership was also unlucky. Tired and dejected, they sat on the seashore wondering what to do next. None of them dared to go to Sugriva for he had warned them not to come back without news of Sita.

As they were unsuccessful in their aim, they decided they would rather die. "Yes! Let us end our lives. At least we have the satisfaction that we were in Rama's service for a short time. Wish we could have died like Jatayu, fighting for Sita's rescue," they said loudly.

At the mention of the name Jatayu, a sea-bird came out from atop the sea-boulders and asked the Vanara prince Angada. "Sir! I am Sampati, Jatayu's elder brother. Did I hear you say that Jatayu was killed by the ten-headed Ravana? I wish I could also have fought against Ravana because I saw him cross the sea along with a beautiful lady. May be she was Sita."

Sampati continued and said, "I know where the wicked Ravana lives. It is an island called Lanka which is very far away. Strong walls have been built around the city and it is difficult to cross them unnoticed." The Vanaras felt happy to know the place.

Jambavanta, an elderly bear-like being, advised Hanuman, "Son! You have the speed of wind. You have the strength to destroy an entire city. You are the only one among us who can fly over the ocean and land on Lanka."

With great enthusiasm Hanuman expanded his chest and sucking in the air, grew bigger and bigger till he seemed to touch the sky. With courage burning in his eyes, he strode atop the tallest peak and with a powerful thrust of his legs, took off. Soon he was air-borne. The Vanara army watched Hanuman's feat with wonder and danced with joy. They blessed this son of Vayu for saving them from humiliation.

# HANUMAN MEETS SITA—
# LANKA IS DESTROYED

Hanuman was also applauded by Suras who showered flower petals on him. The Sun God silently blessed Hanuman by radiating less of heat. The Wind God, Vayu, turned into a gentle breeze in his direction and wished his son success.

To test Hanuman's devotion towards Rama, the Devas sent Surasa, who obstructed Hanuman's flight. She turned herself into a demoness and opened her mouth wide. Hanuman grew bigger in size. She opened her mouth several miles wide and challenged Hanuman that she would let him pass only if he could enter her mouth. Hanuman at once shrunk his body to the size of a thumb and even before Surasa could realise what was happening, Hanuman got in and got out of her mouth. Surasa regained her earlier form and wished him well.

Hanuman encountered several more obstacles but he overcame all of them. He finally landed on Mount Trikuta on which the city of Lanka had been set up.

Lanka was a dazzling city. It had beautiful gardens and parks. The city was surrounded by forts. Fierce looking Rakshasas kept watch day and night and never let any stranger enter the city. So Hanuman decided to turn into a very tiny being and slip past the guards. Soon, it was dark. Hanuman tried to climb over the fort wall and enter Lanka. But he was spotted by Lankini, the protector of Lanka and she tried to stamp him with her massive feet. The enraged Hanuman punched her very hard and with blood running out of her nose and ears, Lankini slumped to the ground. He then quickly entered the city.

Bearing in mind Rama's description of Sita, Hanuman searched for her all over Lanka. But everywhere he found only hideous looking Rakshasis. He then peeped into each and every house but could not find Sita. "Ravana might have forced her to stay in the royal chamber. Let me check there," thought Hanuman, but could not find her there. He closely examined each wife of Ravana, including Mandodari, but none could match the description of Sita. Hanuman got worried. If he were to go back to Rama empty-handed, Rama would die. This would lead to Lakshmana's death too. Unable to bear the news, Bharata, Shatrugna, Kaushalya .... and the entire Ayodhya will die mourning for Rama. Sugriva will end his life unable to bear his friend Rama's death. Hanuman trembled to think of the consequences if he could not find Sita. "Whatever happens, I will not return to Kishkinda unless I have news of Sita," swore Hanuman.

Searching for Sita, Hanuman entered the Ashoka garden. With hundreds of trees, the garden looked beautiful. Under a tree sat a beautiful lady. All her clothes were torn and faded. She looked pale. The beautiful lady was surrounded by ugly looking Rakshasis who kept on praising Ravana in front of her. By then, Hanuman recalled seeing Sita when she had thrown down the ornaments.

He felt happy and relieved that Sita was alive. But at the same time he felt sorry for her condition and also felt sad that a woman like Sita had to undergo such cruelty. Hanuman decided to talk to her when she was alone. So he climbed the tree above her and hid himself amongst the branches.

In a short while, Ravana reached the garden and tried his best to make Sita adore him. Hanuman was so furious to hear his talk that he wanted to kill Ravana at that very spot. Sita even refused to listen to what Ravana was saying, and closing her ears said in a firm voice, "I belong to Rama totally. Rama will definitely come and rescue me. That will be the final day of your life. Get out." The irritated Ravana ordered the Rakshasis to make Sita change her mind. With the exception of a kind Rakshasi called

Trijata, all the others pestered Sita, but in vain. Finally they gave up and went off to sleep. Unable to bear the situation any longer, Sita decided to hang herself from the tree and die.

Hanuman who was watching Sita said softly, "Rama, Rama," Sita looked up and saw a monkey. She thought that Ravana was upto some magic tricks. Hanuman then talked about what Rama's likes and what he did not. Sita's hand which was about to tie the noose, stopped. Hanuman slowly got down from the tree and bowing his head before Sita, introduced himself as Rama's humble servant. To remove any doubts from her mind, Hanuman showed her the ring sent by Rama. Tears of happiness filled up Sita's eyes as soon as she saw her husband's ring. She believed Hanuman when he told her that Rama would soon be waging a war against

Ravana and rescue her from Lanka. She gave Hanuman one of her ornaments and blessed him, "Please convey my love to Rama and ask him to rescue me soon."

Now that Hanuman had met Sita, he decided that he would find out about Ravana's army and his strength and inform Sugriva of them. He had a plan. He provoked all the Rakshasas to attack him and when they did, he jumped on and trampled all the trees in Ashoka garden. The Rakshasas rushed to capture him but he killed them all. When Ravana's commanders-in-chief and other able soldiers tried to catch the monkey, they were defeated and killed. When Ravana heard about the destruction caused by a monkey, he sent his son Indrajit to capture the monkey.

Indrajit was a very skilled warrior, who, at one time, had even defeated Devendra. He used one of his powerful weapons on Hanuman, imprisoned him and dragged him to Ravana's court, When Hanuman was brought before the king, he was very impressed with the ten-headed Ravana. His court was very grand and dazzling. Ravana was sitting on a high throne. As soon as Hanuman came face to face with Ravana, he freed himself from chains and ropes, prepared a high seat out of his very long tail and sat on it.

"O Monkey! Who are you? And why did you destroy the Ashoka garden," asked Ravana. "Sir," replied Hanuman, "I am Rama's messenger. I came to Lanka in search of Sita. You have committed a great mistake by abducting Sita. If you want to live, you return Sita to Rama gracefully and seek refuge in him."

Having warned Ravana thus, Hanuman added, "Listen! I myself could have rescued Sita from here and carried her on my shoulders. But I do not have such orders. Only Rama should do this. And don't underestimate Rama. He is the Lord of the entire universe. Don't seek your own destruction by angering him."

Ravana was very angry. "How dare a monkey talks to a king like me in such a way," he thundered. He ordered his soldiers, "Kill this arrogant Vanara." But Vibhishana, his brother, stopped him, "Brother, he is after all Rama's messenger. A king does not kill a messenger. Instead, you can punish him suitably and let him go back to Rama."

"Yes, brother," agreed Ravana, "What you say makes sense." He then ordered his servants to set fire to Hanuman's long tail and make him walk in the streets of Lanka.

The Rakshasas dipped the monkey's tail in oil and set fire to it. Anjaneya used it as a whip and lashed all the Rakshasas. He then jumped from building to building and reduced them to ashes. he did not even spare Ravana's palace. The whole of Lanka looked like an enormous fire pit.

He only spared the Ashoka garden. He made sure that Sita was safe and after seeking her blessings, left Lanka. He dipped his tall in the sea water, expanded his body, climbed a nearby mountain and with a powerful thrust, flew back.

Hanuman reached Kishkinda and told Rama all about Sita and Ravana's conduct. He conveyed her message and then handed over the ornament Sita had sent as a memento.

Sugriva and the entire Vanara army felt very proud that Hanuman was able to accomplish his mission. Sugriva hugged Hanuman and congratulated him.

# THE WAR

Rama too was very happy that Hanuman was successful in finding Sita. Sugriva had kept up his word and Rama now had to plan about reaching Lanka to kill Ravana and rescue Sita. He therefore talked to Sugriva about this. "Sugriva, you have proved to be my true friend. I want more help from you because I am afraid that Ravana might kill Sita to take revenge. Hence, please get your army ready." Rama called Hanuman also to his side and holding his hands warmly said, "Maruthi, I am so grateful to you for your help. You are the only one among us who is capable of flying across the ocean. So, please tell us how we can get there." Rama also asked his trusted friend about Lanka's city plan, about its main gates, about the trenches built around the fort and many more such information to plan the attack.

Though Hanuman had burnt down Lanka, Ravana had the city rebuilt immediately. Anjaneya who was aware of this told Rama, "Lord! Once we cross the ocean, Lanka will be ours. Have no doubt about it. I shall summon Angada, Neela, Jambavanta and many more valiant Vanaras and bears and will be ready to leave."

Upon Sugriva's order, thousands of Vanaras formed a huge army and walked towards the ocean. But the vast expanse of water stopped them in their march. They just could not think of any method by which they could cross the ocean. They were afraid that they would drown in the water.

In Lanka also, many people were afraid of the consequences of war. They had seen the power of just one monkey. If thousands of such monkeys attacked Lanka, what would be the fate, many wondered. The Rakshasas tried to talk courageously and boasted, "Rama and his Vanaras will be like insects in our hands."

Only one person among them was wise. He was Vibhisana, Ravana's younger brother. He was a devotee of Lord Vishnu and a very righteous man. While the others were advising Ravana about preparing for the war, Vibhisana stood up at the meeting and told his brother, "Ravana, do not act in haste. First and foremost, you have been responsible for this crisis. You have sinned in longing for another man's wife. So, please listen to me. At least now, let us send back Sita to Rama before he attacks. Then peace will prevail on both the sides."

Ravana did not like Vibhisana's words. "I am not a coward. I am not sending Sita back to Rama. Please don't interfere in our plans," he scolded his brother.

Kumbakarna, another brother of Ravana, was also present at the meeting. He was a Rakshasa who slept for six months at a stretch. On waking up, he would eat lots and lots of food and go back to sleep again. Just that day, he had finished one round of sleeping. Though he did not like Ravana's behaviour, he decided to support him out of brotherly love and loyalty.

Vibhisana could not tolerate his brother Ravana provoking war. He again advised him, "Ravana, King of Lanka! Do you know who Sita is. She is a Goddess who can destroy evil. Her husband Sri Rama is the Lord of the Universe. None can fight against him. Not even Kumbakarna or you. So, act sensibly and send back Sita."

Ravana, his son Indrajit and the Rakshasas thought that Vibhisana was behaving like a coward. Vibhisana's frank talk was not liked by anyone. When he once again suggested that Ravana should avoid war with Rama, Ravana was very angry. "Vibhisana, are you really my brother? You talk as if I am your enemy. I feel you are very jealous of me. I would have killed you this very moment. Don't ever step into Lanka again. Get out from, here," he roared.

Feeling sad that his brother ignored his advice, Vibhisana, with four of his followers, went to Rama and sought refuge under him.

"Sir," Vibhisana introduced himself to Rama, "I am Vibhisana, Ravana's brother. I have come to seek refuge under you. I tried my level best to make Ravana realise his mistake. I told him to hand over Sita and made peace with you. He ridiculed me and drove me out of Lanka. Rama, please accept me as your humble servant."

Sugriva and other Vanara leaders did not like this request. So they told Rama, "Rama, Vibhisana belongs to the enemy camp. Moreover he is a Rakshasa and a trickster. So, please think about this before you come to any decision." Hanuman then remembered how Vibhisana had sided him in Ravana's court. So he told Rama, "Rama, Vibhisana has probably approached you as he can become the

king of Lanka after Ravana's death.
He expects you to help him just the
way you helped Sugriva against his
brother Vali. In my humble opinion,
we should accept Vibhisana's
friendship."

Rama agreed with Hanuman and
said, "It is my duty to protect those
who seek refuge in me." On hearing
these words, Vibhisana fell at Rama's
feet and thanked him for this gesture.

Sri Rama embraced Vibhisana and promised him that upon Ravana's death he would be the king of Lanka. He then asked his friend about Ravana's army and Vibhisana explained everything in detail to him.

Under Vibhisana's guidance, the Vanaras built a bridge across the sea by placing logs of wood and big stones. In a few days the bridge was ready. Cheering with excitement, the Vanara army crossed the sea and reached Lanka.

As soon as the Vanara army reached the gates of Lanka, Rama divided them into battalions and placed each group at important places. The whole area echoed with the sound of conches being blown and bows being stringed. These sounds created a scare in the minds of the Rakshasas.

A fierce battle broke out between

the Vanaras and the Rakshasas. Each one of the Vanaras fought bravely and injured or killed many Rakshasas. Sugriva, Hanuman, Angad and Neel killed many Rakshasas and everytime they killed, they cried out, "Victory to Sri Rama!"

The Rakshasas fought equally well. Especially at night, they used their magical powers and were responsible for the death of many Vanaras. But the death toll in Ravana's army was very, very high.

This upset Ravana very much because he had thought that it was very easy to defeat an army of monkeys. But his son Indrajit swore that Rama and Lakshmana would both be dead before dawn. This filled Ravana with delight. He embraced his son and told him, "Indrajit, I am very proud of you. May success be yours!"

Indrajit used the darkness of the night and fought the war with skill and valour. Many Vanaras died at his hands. Indrajit then employed serpent-like arrows which entwined themselves around Rama and Lakshmana as snakes. The poison emitted by these snakes made Rama and Lakshmana lose consciousness. Both of them fell to the ground. Taking them to be dead, Indrajit conveyed this good news to his father. Needless to say, Ravana was extremely happy. This news was conveyed to Sita and she was brought in a flying-machine to show her the fate of her husband and her brother-in-law. She was grief-stricken that her dearest husband was dead.

Soon, the news that Rama and Lakshmana were found dead in the battlefield spread in Lanka. But only Vibhisana knew that Rama and

Lakshmana had lost consciousness.
Soon Rama regained consciousness
but Lakshmana had not recovered
from the snake poison. His body was
slowly turning blue and Rama was
extremely worried. The Devas who
were watching this from the heaven
instructed Garuda to save Rama and
Lakshmana from the snakes. When
the snakes saw that Garuda was about
to swoop down on them, they unwound
themselves and disappeared into
snake pits. Rama and Lakshmana
soon regained consciousness. Garuda
warned them to be careful about
Indrajit and flew into the high skies
again.

Ravana sent many more
Rakshasas, who were very good at
warfare. But each one of them, died
at the hands of Hanuman, Neela and
other valiant Vanaras. Ravana felt
very humiliated. He immediately

rushed to Kumbakama who was fast asleep. With great difficulty, Ravana woke up his brother. "Kumbakarna, if you love me, go and kill my enemies," he ordered.

Kumbakarna had to obey his brother. So he got out of his enormous bed and walked towards the battlefield. He was so huge and massive, it appeared as if a big mountain had entered the battlefield. Kumbakarna lifted Sugriva and Hanuman easily. He thrashed Hanuman on the ground and tucked Sugriva under his arm, who narrowly escaped. The enraged Kumbakarna challenged Rama and a fierce battle was fought. Rama used one of his powerful weapons and chopped Kumbakarna"s arms and legs. He used another weapon which separated Kumbakarna's head from his body.

Kumbakarna soon died. The Vanaras felt very happy at this success.

Ravana was shocked to hear about Kumbakarna's death. He sent his sons Devanthaka, Naranthaka, Trishiraska and Atikaya to the battlefield. But they were no match for the Vanaras and soon Ravana received news about their deaths too. Ravana was terribly shaken by these losses. Grief-stricken, he slumped to the ground. Indrajit who saw his father lose courage, tried to instil some confidence in him and said, "Father, as long as I am alive, please do not think of defeat. This time, my arrows will not spare Rama and Lakshmana. I will soon be back victorious."

Apart from being very brave and very good at warfare, Indrajit also possessed immense magical powers. While his arrows hit Rama and

Lakshmana and caused some injuries,
he used his magical powers upon the
entire Vanara army. He spread a
poisonous gas in the air and soon most
of the Vanaras including Rama and
Lakshmana tumbled down.
Jambavantha, who was fighting at the
other end quickly called Hanuman and
told him, "Maruthi, you cross the
ocean, go to Kailash mountain and
from there fetch a rare herb called
_Sanjivini._ We can then bring back all
the Vanaras to life." Even before
Jambavanta finished saying this,
Hanuman flew across with the speed
of wind and since he could not find
_Sanjivini,_ transported the entire
mountain to Lanka. Very soon, Rama,
Lakshmana and the Vanaras were up
on their feet, fit and fighting.

Indrajit once again used his
magical powers and turned a Rakshasi
to look exactly like Sita. He then took

this fake Sita to the battlefield and in full view of Rama, Lakshmana, Hanuman, Sugriva and others, severed her head.

The Vanaras were aghast. Rama turned numb with shock and Lakshmana vowed to kill Indrajit then and there. He chased Indrajit to a temple where Indrajit acquired more secret powers. Lakshmana destroyed this secret power by using a suitable weapon and also struck down Indrajit's head. The Vanaras rejoiced at this triumph. Rama felt very relieved that Lakshmana had come to no harm and also that it was not Sita who had died at Indrajit's hands.

Indrajit's death was the severest blow to Ravana. He had lost all his sons, his brothers and his army in the war. The whole of Lanka plunged into sorrow. Some criticised Surpanakha

for provoking Ravana into kidnapping
Sita. Others cursed Ravana for his
misdeed. "His lust for a woman has
caused us so much agony," lamented
the citizens for there was death and
destruction in each and every house
in Lanka.

Ravana climbed into his chariot
and entered the battlefield with a
fierce determination to kill Rama. But
first of all, he had to encounter
Lakshmana. Ravana stopped the
arrows used by Lakshmana in mid-
air. He then turned his attention
towards Rama. Severe fighting broke
out between Rama and Ravana.
Ravana used many powerful arrows
but Rama could stop each one of them
in mid-air. The arrows would become
useless and fall down. But then, even
Rama's arrows were futile as they
could not penetrate the armour worn

by Ravana. This was an armour granted to Ravana by Brahma as a boon and ordinary arrows could not penetrate through it.

With Ravana and Rama both being equally powerful, the battle between them became very fierce and raged on for several days. Even the celestial

gods watched them anxiously as the war did not seem to end at all. But slowly Ravana felt drained of energy and knew that his end was close at hand. Still he fought. Finally Rama used *Brahmastra,* the mightiest of all mighty weapons. It tore the armour worn by Ravana and hit him in the chest. The mighty Ravana fell down and died. The evil was vanquished.

The Devas rejoiced over the death of this wicked Rakshasa. The Vanaras went berserk with joy. Only Vibhisana, Mandodari and Ravana's other queens were plunged into grief.

On Rama's advice, Vibhisana performed Ravana's last rites.

Rama who was the incarnation of Lord Vishnu thus brought peace to the land. All the Rishis and Devas rejoiced that the Rakshasas had been wiped out.

Rama kept up his word and crowned Vibhisana as the king of Lanka.

Sri Rama then sent Hanuman to fetch Sita. Sitadevi was very happy that the wicked Ravana had been killed. She looked forward to rejoin her beloved Rama. But he did not

accept her immediately. He wanted to test whether she had remained devout to him. So he said, "I find it impossible to believe that a Rakshasa like Ravana had not touched a beautiful woman like you. You are impure, so, I cannot accept you back as my wife." Rama's cruel words filled Sita's heart with sadness. She had given up food and water and had barely kept herself alive only to reunite with Rama. If he suspected her virtue, then life was not worth living for her. So the distressed Sita turned towards Lakshmana and asked him to prepare a pyre for her. Rama did not object.

Sita jumped into the pyre and prayed to Agni, the God of Fire to rescue her only if she had remained pure. Kubera, Yama, Varuna, Indra, Shiva, Brahma and other Gods and Goddesses who witnessed this scene from the sky, came down to earth and conveyed their displeasure to Rama. "Ramachandra! You are the wisest among the wise. You are the Lord of the Universe. How could you behave like a mere human being? How could you watch Sita jump into the fire?" they asked him. Brahma placed his hand on Rama's shoulder and told him, "You are Narayana. Sita is Lakshmi. As a divine couple, you are far above suspicions and distrust." By then, Agni gently carried Sita out of the pyre and told, "Rama, Sita is chaste. Please accept her." Rama's doubts were cleared, and joyfully he accepted Sita.

Rama, Sita and Lakshmana were blessed by all the Gods. Rama's exile had come to an end. So he bade good-bye to all his Vanara friends and thanked Vibhisana for his help.

Rama, Sita and Lakshmana,

accompanied by Sugriva and Hanuman left for Ayodhya in a Pushpak Viman arranged by Vibhisana. On their flight, Sita and Rama identified the places they had stayed during the exile. Rama also showed her the Rishyamukha, Pampa Lake, Sabari's Ashram and Kishkinda and the forests where he had roamed pining for Sita.

The Pushpak Viman reached Ayodhya. Bharata was waiting for Rama's return. He prostrated before his brother and begged him to take charge of the kingdom. Kaushalya, Kaikeyi, Sumitra and Vashishtha blessed Rama and with their consent, Rama agreed to become the king.

Soon Rama was crowned the king of Ayodhya. The Coronation was conducted on a grand scale. Rama and Sita were seated on the throne.

Lakshmana, Bharata and Shatrugna
stood behind them. Hanuman sat at
Rama's feet.

People rejoiced about this happy
event. The festivities continued for a
week and Rama made generous gifts
to everyone.

Sri Rama ruled over Ayodhya for many years. People lived a happy, contented life in the kingdom and this glorious reign was hailed as RAMA RAJYA.

*This is the story of RAMAYANA. This epic was written by Maharshi Valmiki, Reading Ramayana will help us to follow Rama's ideals, his devotion towards his parents, his values and his truthfulness. Let us all strive to be better human beings.*

☛ *Please turnover the book for Mahabharata*

# EXERCISES

## I. ANSWER THE FOLLOWING QUESTIONS

1. Why did Vishwamitra wanted to take Rama with him?

2. How did Rama succeed at Sita's swayamvar?

3. What happened when Parashurama confronted Rama?

4. How did Manthara poison Kaikeyi's mind against Rama's coronation?

5. How did Kaikeyi compel Dasharatha to send Rama into exile?

6. Describe the scene briefly when Rama leaves Ayodhya with Sita and Lakshmana to live in the forest.

7. Why did Sravana Kumar's father curse king Dasharatha? How did it come true?

8. What did Bharatha do on learning of Rama's exile?

9. How did Surpanaka poison Ravana's mind to kidnap Sita?

10. How did Ravana succeed in kidnapping Sita?

11. What happened when Rama and Lakshmana chopped off Kabandha's hands?

12. Why was Vali angry with Sugriva?

13. How did Rama help Sugriva to regain his kingdom?

14. How did Hanuman locate Sita?

15. What happened when Hanuman's tail was set on fire in Ravana's court?

16. Why did Vibhisana advice Ravana to send back Sita to Rama?

17. How did the Vanara army cross the ocean to reach Lanka?

18. How did Indrajit knock down Rama and Lakshmana? Who killed him in the end?

19. Describe briefly the fight between Rama and Ravana.

20. What happened when Rama doubted Sita's purity?

## II. ACTIVITY

Enact the following scenes on stage

i    Sita's swayamvar

ii)  Rama's leaving Ayodhya

iii) Ravana kidnapping Sita

iv) Hanuman in Ravana's court

v)  Final fight between Rama and Ravana

## III. WHO SAID THIS TO WHOM AND WHEN

1. "A king should never fall a prey to vices. He should treat each and everyone with respect and rule the kingdom well."

2. "Are you playing a joke on me."

3. "Please do not leave me behind. I will also come with you to the forest. Ayodhya will be like hell to me without you."

4. "Mother, where is Father? What has happened in my absence?"

5. "Why have you brought such a huge army? If you plan to attack Rama, you will have to defeat me first."

6. "Please treat our mother Kaikeyi well. Be happy. Be kind to others."

7. "But dear sister, who caused you all these injuries and why?"

8. "My lady, please hand over the alms to me here."

9. "Please convey my love to Rama and ask him to rescue me soon."

10. "It is my duty to protect those who seek refuge in me."

* * *

# MAHABHARATA

Exercises at the end

## FOR

2 in 1

## CHILDREN

### Vatsala Iyengar

🌐 Vasan Publications

Rs. 75/-

© Vasan publications,
Edition : 2013

*Published by:*

**Vasan Publications**

# 25,  Vasan Towers, Goods Shed Road,
Bangalore - 560 053,  Ph.080- 2670 5679
e-mail : info@mastermindbooks.com
www.mastermindbooks.com

D.T.P :
Sunshine

Printed at:
Srinidhi Graphics

# CONTENTS

Bhishma's Vow.................................................... 5

Amba's revenge..................................................11

Pandavas-Kauravas.............................................15

Gurukul-The school.............................................18

Duryodhana's plot...............................................24

The Thumb........................................................27

Karna-Duryodhana..............................................32

The Wax Mansion...............................................44

Draupadi's Swayamvar.........................................53

The Rajasuya Yagna............................................62

The Gamble.......................................................70

The exile...........................................................82

The Slaying of Kichaka........................................90

To the defence of Virata.......................................96

Krishna's mediation...........................................106

The Kurukshetra War.........................................117

# Our Other Useful Publications

# Bhishma's Vow

This is not a recent story. It is a very ancient story which occurred thousands of years ago.

Santanu was the king of Hastinapur. He was wise, kind and just. All the citizens loved him and respected him. The river Goddess Ganga was Santanu's first wife. Santanu had met Ganga at the river bank, fallen in love with her and had proposed marriage to her. But then, Ganga had laid down certain conditions to say "Yes" to her proposal and had warned him that whatever she did, he was not to counter-question her. So desperate was the king to marry her that without a moment's hesitation, he agreed to obey her conditions.

Ganga was a beautiful woman. She was also a devout wife and looked after

the king with love and affection. They were so happy that Santanu even forgot that a year had already passed. He also forgot about his promise to Ganga. Meanwhile, Ganga gave birth to a baby boy. The king's happiness knew no bounds as he fondly looked at his heir. But his joy was short-lived. The same night Ganga carried the baby and headed towards the river. Santanu was perplexed. So he followed her. By the time he could realise her intentions, she had thrown the baby into the river. Santanu was about to ask her the reason for her attitude when he remembered his promise to her at the time of their marriage. He could not question her about anything. Both of them returned to the palace silently.

Even after this incident, Santanu's love for Ganga did not diminish in any way. But he was perplexed about her

behaviour.How could she kill her own child? Was she a demon or a human, he wondered. Nevertheless, he decided to forget about this incident and continued to lead a happy life with Ganga. Subsequently, Ganga gave birth to another baby boy. The baby met a similar fate as the first born. Santanu turned pale with worry. But still, he did not have the courage to question Ganga. He felt very sad and depressed.

Ganga gave birth to seven baby boys, one year after another. But all the babies were thrown into the river a few hours after their birth. And it was none other than their own mother who killed them.

When Ganga gave birth to a baby boy for the eighth time, Santanu could no longer bear the situation. By then, he had already been a dejected man. When Ganga was about to throw the newborn into the river, Santanu stopped her and asked her, "Do you know what you are doing? Are you a demon? You have killed seven sons of ours. I can no longer bear it. I will save at least this child." He could not control his emotions.

Ganga was angry with Santanu because he dared question her actions. "I will not live with you even for another moment," she said. Santanu loved Ganga very much. He was grief-striken. He begged and pleaded with her not to

desert him. But Ganga told the king that she had to return to her abode as she had fulfilled her task upon the earth. She then explained to Santanu what her task was.

Long ago, there were eight demi-gods known as Ashta-Vasus. Once, out of sheer greed, they wanted to steal Vashista's cow. The youngest of them, by name Prabhasa stole the cow. Vashista was enraged at this and cursed them to be born as human-beings upon the earth. When the Vasus sought to be forgiven, the sage relented and laid down that the seven Vasus could live only for a few hours upon the earth but Prabhasa was to lead his entire life upon the earth.

These Ashta-Vasus were the babies born to Ganga. The seven Vasus were thrown into the river and Prabhasa was the only survivor.

Ganga narrated this episode to Santanu and disappeared after promising him that she would hand over Prabhasa to his care subsequently.

Seven years later, Santanu witnessed a young lad practising archery by the riverside. A strong feeling attracted him towards the boy. At that moment, Ganga appeared before the king and told him, "Here is your son Devavrat. He is not an ordinary person. He will earn fame as a great man. Look after him well." She then returned to her abode.

Santanu was immensely happy. Hugging the child, his heart swelled with love and affection. He took his son to the palace and looked after him well.

Devavrat grew up to be a brave and courageous boy. Santanu had appointed a master for him. Devavrat thirsted for

knowledge and excelled himself in all fields of education. As a true Kshatriya, he also perfected warfare and was hailed as the mightiest of all. Truthful and honest, he gained the respect of one and all. At the opportune time, Santanu crowned Devavrat as the heir-prince.

Meanwhile, Santanu had gone on a hunt. Near the river, he saw an extremely beautiful girl. She was the daughter of Dasaraja, a fisherman. Santanu fell in love with her and sent a messenger to her father asking her hand in marriage.

"I am prepared to have my daughter wed the king," said Dasaraja. "But I have a condition," he added, "I want my daughter to be the queen and the child born to her as the future king. If your king doesn't agree to this, ask him to forget about marrying my daughter."

Santanu was worried. He found it impossible to live without Satyavati, Dasaraja's daughter. But how could he marry her? For he had already crowned Devavrat as the heir to the throne. There were none to equal Devavrat for the throne. So, Santanu decided not to accept the condition laid down by Dasaraja. But he felt very depressed about losing Satyavati. He lost interest in the affairs of the kingdom. Even hunting, dance or music did not interest him. Only Satyavati's immense beauty haunted him.

Devavrat knew his father's state of mind. So he met Dasaraja and pleaded with him to get Satyavati married to the king. Dasaraja was adamant. "Are you prepared to give up the throne for the sake of your father's happiness?" he asked.

Devavrat did not hesitate. "If it can bring happiness to my father, I do not want the throne. I am prepared to give it up. I swear," he said. But Dasaraja was not convinced.

He asked Devavrat, "O! Prince, it is easy for you to say that you do not want the throne. But you will get married and have children. Later on, your children will also have children. And if they claim their right over the throne, what will be the fate of Satyavati's children?"

Devavrat agreed with Dasaraja's thinking. He felt that it was a fair question. He thought for a while and said, "Respected Sir, have no doubts about this. I hereby swear that I will be a bachelor throughout my life. I will never get married."

This decision by young Devavrat to lead his life all alone for the sake of his

father's happiness drew appreciation from all the Suras. This vow came to be known as 'Bhishma's Vow.' Devavrat was henceforth called as Bhishma.

Bhishma returned to the palace and performed the marriage of Satyavati to his father. In the presence of hundreds of citizens, he again proclaimed that he was giving up his rights to the throne. Highly pleased with his son's sacrifice, Santanu embraced Bhishma and blessed him as *lccha Marani**. "Let not death near you as long as you want it," he wished.

Bhishma lived through the ages as a great son of India.

---

* *lccha Marani :* - One who could die only when and if he desired to die.

# Amba's revenge

Santanu and Satvavati led a happy married life. Subsequently Satyavati gave birth to two sons. The eldest was Chitrangadh. After the demise of Santanu, Bhishma crowned Chitrangadh as the King. But the king died shortly thereafter. So, Bhishma coronated Vichitravirya, the second son, as the king. But since the boy was still young, Bhishma ruled the land on his behalf. There was peace and prosperity everywhere.

Several years passed. Vichitravirya was now a young man and was of marriageable age.

The king of Kashi had three daughters by the names of Amba, Ambika and Ambalika, who were renowned for their beauty. A duel was arranged and the king proclaimed that

he would give his daughters in marriage to the winner of this duel. Bhishma heard about this and set forth to Kashi. He defeated all the other princes and left for Hastinapur along with the three princesses.. On the way, Shalvaraj challenged him to a war because he wanted to marry Amba. But Bhishma defeated him and reached Hastinapur.

Actually, Bhishma had selected these princesses as brides for Vichitravirya. But Amba wanted to marry Shalvaraj and indicated this to Bhishma. She also requested him to send her to Shalvaraj. On hearing this, Bhishma did not want to force her into an unwilling marriage with Vichitravirya. So he sent her back to Shalvaraj. But Shalvaraj was not prepared to accept her. "You can live with whoever carried you away," he scorned. He had not forgotten his

humiliation at the hands of Bhishma.
Amba returned to Hastinapur with a
heavy heart. Bhishma felt sorry for her.
By then, Vichitravirya had also decided
not to marry Amba. She could not bear
the humiliation. So she pleaded with
Bhishma to marry her. But how could
he? Hadn't he taken a vow not to marry?
He said 'no' to her.

This infuriated Amba. She held
Bhishma totally responsible for her
plight. Hatred and revenge filled her
thoughts. She sought the help of other
Kings to wage a war against Bhishma,
but none supported her. Her anger
against Bhishma grew stronger. In
desperation, she observed a very strict
penance, praying to Lord Shiva. Her sole
purpose was to kill Bhishma with her
own hands.

Pleased with Amba's penance, Shiva
appeared before her. But the boon she

wanted was against the divine spirit. "Bhishma has the blessings of all Gods and Goddesses," said Shiva, hence, nobody can kill him. But all humans on this earth are bound to die sooner or later. You can kill Bhishma. But not now. You can do so in your next birth upon this earth. You will be born as a daughter to Drupada, the king of Panchala. Your wish will then be fulfilled."

Amba had only one aim in her life that to kill Bhishma. She was prepared to wait until even her next re-birth. She therefore headed straight to Drupada's palace and jumped into the sacrificial fire (yagna) being conducted there. Her body was reduced to ashes.

Amba was born as Drupada's daughter and waited for an opportunity to seek vengeance on Bhishma.

# The Pandavas and the Kauravas

Vichitravirya had two sons. The eldest was Dhritarashtra, born blind. Hence Bhishma crowned the second son, Pandu, as the king. Pandu was a very capable king and ruled the land well.

Vichitravirya had a son by name Vidura through a chamber maid. Vidura was an able statesman and a scholar. He acted as an advisor to Pandu. Bhishma was the father figure to all of them.

Kunthi, daughter of the king of Mathura was Pandu's wife. Prior to her marriage, a sage had taught her some mantras. He had indicated to her that by chanting these, Kunthi could summon any celestial God and beget a son from him. Just to test the veracity

of this, the young Kunthi invited Surya, the Sun God and acquired a son from him. But being a virgin, she feared social outcry against her and placed the baby, which had been born with a pair of brilliant ear ornaments, in a wooden box and gently pushed it into the river. Floating on the river, the box reached the hands of a childless charioteer. He handed the baby to his wife Radha. The couple named the boy as Karna because of his ear-ornaments and brought him up with love and affection.

According to a royal custom, Pandu took another wife Madri. But because of a curse, he could not father any child. Seeing his plight, Kunthi confided to him about the mantra taught to her. So, he urged her and Madri to use these mantras.With the result, Kunthi had three sons born of gods - Dharmaraj from Yama, Bhima from Vayu, the wind

God and Arjun from Devendra. Madri gave birth to two sons Nakul and Sahadev. These five sons of Pandu were the Pandavas. All of them were handsome, noble and courageous.

Because of his curse, Pandu had given up his kingdom and was living in the forest. He did not live for long. He died when the Pandavas were still youngsters. Entreating Kunthi to be a mother to all the five sons of Pandu, Madri burnt herself on the funeral pyre of her husband.On hearing about the death of Pandu and Madri, Bhishma and Vidur hastened to the forest and brought Kunthi and the Pandavas to Hastinapur.

Dhritarashtra had one hundred sons by the name of Kauravas. His wife was Gandhari.The eldest of the Kauravas was Duryodhana who, from a very young age, had nursed a deep

hatred for the Pandavas, and that is why he could not tolerate the Pandavas in Hastinapur. Pretending to be friendly with them, he plotted devious means of getting rid of them from the kingdom.

## Gurukul-The School

It is very important for the Kshatriyas, that is the warrior clan, to be proficient in archery and sword fencing. We already know that the Pandavas and the Kauravas were being brought up together by Bhishma. He always showed keen interest in their education and proficiency in warfare. He therefore wanted the best among the tutors to train Pandavas and Kauravas in archery and sword fighting.

One day, all the princes were playing the ball game together and the ball fell into a dilapidated well. How to take out

the ball was their problem. Just at that time, they spotted a Brahmin. He was a thin person, but his bright eyes and the glow on his face indicated a brilliant man. The Brahmin listened to the children and said in a teasing voice, "You are from a warrior clan and still you do not know how to take out the ball from the well!" The children were surprised. What is the relationship between the ball and the warrior clan, they wondered. They raised this doubt with the Brahmin. He replied, "Let me show you."

The Brahmin was not an ordinary person. He pulled out a blade of gross and after chanting a mantra, threw it into the well. The gross hit the ball with a lot of force and the ball bounced out of the well. The princes realised that he was an extraordinary man. They wanted to know his name. But the Brahmin

smiled and said, "Go to your grandfather Bhishma and narrate this incident to him. He will know who I am."

It didn't take long for Bhishma to know the identity of this Brahmin. He was none other than Dronacharya. Bhishma knew that no one could match Drona's skill in archery in the whole country. So, Bhishma hastened to meet Dronacharya and appointed him as the tutor for the princes. All the princes felt

happy and proud that they were Dronacharya's disciples.

Among all the princes, Arjun was Dronacharya's favourite disciple. Arjun always aimed his bow very well. He always respected his Guru. And though the other princes received good training from their master, it was Arjun who excelled himself in archery.

Previously Drona had a friend by name Drupada. They were fellow students under Bharadhwaja. Drupada the prince of Panchala had promised Drona that in proof of their true friendship, he would share his kingdom with Drona when he ascended the throne.

After completing his education, Drona married Kripacharya's sister. A son was born to the couple and he was named as Ashwathama. To ensure a

good life for his son, Drona decided to employment under a king. He then remembered Drupada and also recalled his promise about sharing the kingdom. But when he went to meet Drupada, a rude shock awaited him. Drupada refused to recognise him. "I do not know who you are," he said. "People will laugh if you say you are a friend of mine, because you are a beggar and I am the king." Drona, a great scholar and a great warrior felt very humiliated., He did not want to stay there even for a moment. He went straight to Kripacharya and poured out all his anguish to him.

Ever since this incident, Drona waited for an opportunity to teach a lesson for Drupada's arrogance. With brave Arjun, with Duryodhana who was good at the mace, with the powerful Bhima and with courageous Yudhistira

as students, Drona felt that the time was right for him to seek his revenge against Drupada. So, first of all, he ordered Duryodhana to wage a war against the Panchala king and drag him by the hair through the battlefield. But Duryodhana was no match for Drupada and was easily defeated by him. Disappointed, Drona entrusted this task to Arjun.

It did not take long for Arjun to defeat Drupada. He imprisoned the king and produced him before Drona. Drupada felt punished. All the insults that he had heaped on Drona flashed through his mind. He stood before Drona with a bowed head.

Since Drupada was defeated in the war. Drona had the right to claim the entire kingdom as his own. But he was an unselfish person. So he told Drupada, "My friend, let one half of the kingdom be with you. I will retain the other half

so that both of us can be equals. Then you will have no hesitation in accepting me as your friend."

This generous attitude of Drona made Drupada feel all the more humiliated. But instead of being grateful to him, a feeling of revenge grew strong in Drupada. He craved for a son who would be able to kill Drona.

## Duryodhana's Plot

Right from the day the Pandavas entered Hastinapur, the Kauravas, especially Duryodhana, disliked them intensely. He was also extremely jealous of the Pandavas for they had earned the love and respect of the entire kingdom. By some means or the other, he wanted to kill the Pandavas, especially Bhima. But Duryodhana was fully aware that it would not be possible to kill Bhima

through a wrestling match or with the mace. So Duryodhana had a sinister plot in mind.

One day, Duryodhana invited the Pandavas for a holiday by the riverside. Pandavas were unaware of Duryodhana's devious plan. Thinking about all the enjoyment, they readily agreed. And what a lot of fun it was! Horse-riding;, boating, camp fire etc. On the ultimate day, Duryodhana had arranged for a royal feast. Bhima, who was a glutton, could not resist the many mouth-watering delicacies and sweet dishes. Happily, he ate and ate but did not know that a deadly poison had been mixed with his food.

In the night, when the others were fast asleep, the Kauravas tied the hands and legs of Bhima and threw him into the river.

The next morning Yudhistira found Bhima missing from his bed. Presuming that he had loitered away, the other Pandavas returned to the palace along with Kauravas.

Bhima, who had sunk to the bottom of the river had lost consciousness, but was not dead. Seeing his inert body on the river bed, the king of Nagalok* treated him against the poison. The king knew of Duryodhana's evil intentions and hence warned Bhima to be careful about Duryodhana and his brothers. Bhima, on recovering his strength and power, thanked the residents of Nagalok for their hospitality and returned to Hastinapur.

Dharmaraj, Kunthi and the other Pandavas who were immensely worried about Bhima's strange

---

* *Nagalok : - A serpent world under the earth*

disappearance were very happy to see him back. Duryodhana was baffled that Bhima had survived such a strong poison.

Certain about Duryodhana's hatred and jealousy, Bhima warned his brothers and mother about the danger posed by the Kauravas.

This incident made Duryodhana all the more determined to kill the Pandavas as he knew that they were the rightful heirs to the throne of Hastinapur..

It was under these circumstances that Duryodhana met Karna.

## The Thumb

Hiranyadhanu was the king of Nishada. Hunting was the main occupation of his people, as they were tribals. Ekalavya was the only son

of Hiranyadhanu. It was his ardent desire to learn the art of archery from Dronacharya.

So, one day he travelled to Hastinapur and witnessed Drona teaching the Pandavas and the Kauravas - the art of archery. Ekalavya went straight to Drona and requested him to include him among his disciples. Drona questioned Ekalavya about his caste and creed. And he turned down the request on the ground that he taught only the Kshatriyas. Disappointed, Ekalavya returned to the forest. He then made a statue of Drona in mud and installed it at the place where he usually practised archery. Everyday he prostrated before the statue and practised archery. His concentration was so high that he could gained mastery over archery and acquired immense knowledge about it.

One day, Drona took his pupils to the forest to teach them hunting. It was the same forest where Ekalavya practised archery. Inside the forest Drona observed bow marks on the tree barks indicating archery practice. Just then, a hound standing near Drona started barking. Within a moment the hound's mouth was covered by seven arrows. Drona was astonished to find that someone had used his bow in the right direction and the exact place just by listening to the barking sound. Drona was therefore very curious to know more about this archer who had even excelled his own disciples.

Arjun who was standing next to Drona was baffled. "I will ensure that none can equal you in archery," was Drona's assurance to Arjun. But was he teaching someone else secretly wondered Arjun.

Both Drona and Arjun went in search of the archer. They saw Ekalavya and introduced themselves to him,, Ekalavya was delighted. He felt as if he had found a treasure and putting down the bow, prostrated before his Guru. Drona was immensely pleased. He asked Ekalavya, "Son! You are an excellent archer. Who is your Guru?"

His guru was right in front of him. But instead, Ekalavya took Drona to the statue and said, "Sir, my Guru is none other than Dronacharya, an expert archer and an unparalleled warrior. I have prepared his statue out of mud and imagining his physical presence, I practice archery", replied Ekalavya in a humble voice.

Drona then recalled Ekalavya's earlier request to teach him archery. He instructed the boy to exhibit his talent. Ekalavya obeyed his instructions and

demonstrated his skill with the bow and the arrow. All the princes present there were astonished with his skill.

Drona too could not believe his own eyes. He admired the achievement by a tribal. He called Ekalavya to come nearer and said "Son! I am Drona, I am the Guru you are talking about. Since you say that you learnt it from me, shouldn't you pay me my Gurudakshina?*"

Ekalavya in reply said, "Respected Sir, I am at your bidding. Whatever you want, I will give it to you."

Drona wanted to impair Ekalavya's capability to use the bow and the arrow. This would also remove any challenges to Arjun's supremacy over the skill. He therefore said, "Ekalavya, cut your right thumb and offer it to me as your fee."

---

* *Gurudakshina :* - fee offering to the teacher

Ekalavya realised Drona's intentions, but without any hesitation, he chopped his right thumb and willingly offered it to Drona.

Drona was immensely pleased with Ekalavya's devotion and after complementing him about this, returned to the palace along with his disciples.

## Karna and Duryodhana

Whenever people talk about friendship, they always refer to Karna and Duryodhana. For, they had a very strong bond of friendship between them.

Drona had taught the princes everything about warfare. He had also told them about the methods to be followed during a war. He had explained about the right and the

wrong, the do's and the don'ts a Kshatriya should follow. Arjun attained excellence in archery under Drona's training. Dharmaraja was adept at fighting from atop a chariot. Bhima and Duryodhana acquired mastery in using the mace. Nakul and Sahadev were good as horse-riders.

Drona wanted the entire Hastinapur to know about the expertise of the princes in waging wars. So he made suitable arrangements for such a day.

On the appointed day, the citizens of Hastinapur flocked to the arena of war sports. For, they had an opportunity to watch the princes demonstrate individually, their skill and knowledge. And compete with each other.

Dhritharashtra, Gandhari, Kunthi, Vidhura, Bhishma, Kripa and Drona were seated on the dais. The commoners

were also provided with seats. The entire Hastinapur wore a festive look.

Shortly, all the princes, that is Dharmaraja with his four brothers and Dhuryodhana accompanied by his ninety-nine brothers entered the arena. They were all dressed in a war-like fashion and were armed suitably.

The competition began after the Vedic chant by the Raj Purohit.* Conches were sounded and drums were beaten to indicate the opening of the games. It was then announced that the princes should exhibit their capabilities. The archers, the fencers, the wrestlers amongst the princes demonstrated their talent. "Bravo! Bravo," shouted the excited crowd. Bhima's and Duryodhana's deftness in using the mace also delighted the crowd. Nakul,

---

* Chief priest of the palace

Sahadev and the other Kauravas also drew appreciation from the spectators.

It was now Arjun's turn. Partha (Arjun) was Drona's prize student. When he entered the arena, the spectators clapped their hands and cried out, "Hail Arjun! Hail Arjun!." Arjun, the warrior, demonstrated before the public all that he had learned from his teacher. The crowd applauded each and every feat of Arjun. Kunthi felt very happy and proud of him.

The only person who could not tolerate this adulation towards Arjun was Duryodhana. He felt restless and agitated, that none of his younger brothers could excel Arjun. If he were to score victory over the Pandavas, he ought to have a very able person who could defeat Arjun. Otherwise his ambition to rule Hastinapur would be shattered, thought Duryodhana.

Suddenly a man stood up from amongst the spectators and entering the arena proclaimed that he too would like to demonstrate his skill as a warrior and prove himself to be far better than Arjun.

Drona was annoyed that a stranger trespassed into the arena which was meant only for the princes. He was all the more angry that this stranger had ridiculed Arjun. But Arjun accepted this challenge from a newcomer and Drona had no other option but to give permission. But he was curious to know more about this person whose face radiated an inner strength. He had a pair of ear rings which dazzled in the sunlight. He was Karna.

These dazzling ear rings also caught the attention of Kunthi and it immediately occurred to her that the stranger was none other than her eldest

born. She was filled with anguish to her two children facing each other in a challenge.

When Karna displayed all the feats of Arjun effortlessly, Duryodhana was delighted. "Finally, I have found someone who can combat with Arjun," he rejoiced. He immediately went to Karna and embracing him said, "From now on, you are my brother."

The contest between Arjun and Karna created a lot of excitement amongst the spectators. They knew that this would be a very significant contest, for both Arjun and Karna were great warriors.

Kunthi, the mother for both Karna and Arjun just couldn't witness the scene. She knew for certain that Karna was the child she had set adrift in the river long ago. Moreover, at close

quarters one could make out a striking resemblance between the two brothers. Thinking about the outcome, she fainted.

Suddenly an idea occurred to Drona. He decided that he would allow only princes to take part in this contest. He immediately conveyed this suggestion to Kripa. Kripa at once entered the arena and told Arjun, "Arjun! Dronacharya has agreed to this combat. But prior to this, both of you have to proclaim about yourselves."

Arjun had no difficulty in proclaiming about his royal origin. It was now Karna's turn to reply. The warrior told the spectators that his name was Karna. But what next? He did not know who his real parents were, what his clan was, or any other information about himself. Red in the face, Karna felt distressed that fate had

cheated him. He felt utterly humiliated. Kripa took advantage of this opportunity and spoke again.

"You do not know who you are. You are just an ordinary soldier. So, you do not qualify yourself to take part in a contest meant only for the royal blood. You may leave the arena," he said in an insulting tone.

Drona and Kripa did not have any grudge against Karna. But to avoid Arjun's defeat by this warrior, they had to prevent Karna's participation in the contest.

Karna could not say anything. He did not know who he was, except that he had been brought up by a charioteer.. He had no status in the society.

Duryodhana too, did not like Karna being humiliated in such a fashion. He desperately needed someone to fight

against Arjun. So, he quickly ran upto Karna and said, "I am the prince of Hastinapur and upon my authority, I am appointing you as the king of Anga. You are now a king. So, I dare anyone to say anything against you." So, saying he placed a crown on Karna's head. He also performed all the necessary rites to bestow the kingdom of Anga on Karna.

Bhishma, Drona and Vidura were speechless. The Pandavas found Duryodhana's behaviour very strange. Bhima thought it to be ridiculous. He roared with laughter and said, "A charioteer's son! King of Anga! Ho... Ho......!"

But Duryodhana ignored them all and hugging Karna in a friendly way, drove away in his chariot.

The contest ended and the crowd dispersed. Some praised Arjun, others

Karna but none knew that Karna was the eldest among Kunthi's children."

From that day onwards Duryodhana and Karna became very close friends and Karna remained loyal to his friend till the very last.

Karna was a great warrior and a good human-being. But his only drawback was that he did not know about his origin. He had learnt archery under Parasurama by representing to him that he was a Brahmin. This was because Parasurama hated Kshatriyas and had vowed not to teach anyone of them. Karna became a favourite student of Parasurama and learnt from him the usage of a master weapon known as Brahmastra.

One day Parasurama was taking his afternoon nap reclining on Karna's lap, when a bee bit Karna's thigh. Blood

started flowing but since Karna did not want to disturb his Guru's sleep, he bore the pain without flinching. When the blood oozed to Parasurama's cheek, he woke up, Karna tried to explain his action to his Guru but Parasurama was not convinced. Angered that Karna had told him a lie about being a Brahmin, he cursed his student, "Karna! You have deceived me by uttering a lie. I hereby curse you that whatever you have learnt from me shall fail you when you need it most."

Karna was aghast. All his dedication had become futile. He fell at his Guru's feet. "Please forgive me," he pleaded. "In my determination to seek knowledge from you, I lied about me being a Brahmin." But Parashurama did not relent . "Karna, you have been one of my best students. But I am punishing you for your lie. You may remain a great

warrior. But you will be unable to recall the Brahmastra when you need it most." Dismayed, Karna was forced to give up the school.

Karna was a very generous man. He was reputed for his charity. To test him, Indra once put on the garb of an old man and begged Karna for his ear-rings and armour. Karna donated these without any hesitation. Pleased with his generosity, Indra revealed himself and bade him to ask for any boon.

"I ask for your weapon, the Shaktya," Karna replied. It was a very powerful weapon and had never failed to destroy anything that it touched. Karna wanted to use this weapon against Arjun for he knew beforehand that a war was inevitable between the Pandavas and the Kauravas.

# The Wax Mansion

**P**andava's courage and the love and affection people had showered on them had created a deep jealousy within Duryodhana. His thoughts were always about killing the Pandavas. His plot to poison Bhima had failed. So, he wanted a good plan to wipe them out totally. His brothers aided him in his actions. Dhritarashtra adored his eldest son Duryodhana and could not bring himself to tick off his son though he knew of Duryodhana's evil intentions.

Duryodhana's mother Gandhari also doted on her eldest son and thus Duryodhana fully exploited the love of his parents for his selfishness.

Duryodhana once came to know that a grand festival was being arranged in Varanavati and he decided to use the occasion to achieve his aim. So, he paid

a visit to the Pandavas and praising the beauty of Varanavati, he described the great festival to be conducted there with all the pomp and grandeur. He also told them that the people of the city were eagerly awaiting the Pandavas to grace the occasion. The unsuspecting Pandavas agreed to go, more so, since Dhritarashtra also told them to witness the festival.

Overjoyed that Pandavas had agreed to go to Varanavati, Duryodhana had a palatial mansion built for their stay. It was made of wax and other inflammable material like jute, dry grass *etc.* The idea was to set the mansion on fire at night when the Pandavas were fast asleep and make people believe that it was a fire accident. No one would suspect the Kauravas.

The Pandavas came to know- of this wax house through Vidura. They felt

deeply hurt that their own kith and kin were betraying them. But pretending to be unaware of the danger to their lives, the Pandavas proceeded to Varanavati but tried to find out if there was any escape route from the wax mansion. Luckily for them, Vidura had engaged an expert miner who had dug a tunnel under a chamber leading to a pit in the forest.

Duryodhana had employed many servants to keep a watch over the Pandavas. Kunthi was also staying with her children in the mansion and hence the Pandavas familiarized themselves thoroughly with the tunnel route, somehow or the other escaping the attention of the guards.

Within a few days, Vidura sent a secret word to the Pandavas informing them about the precise day on which the mansion was to be set on fire. That

night, Kunthi prepared a feast for all the servants in which an intoxicating powder had been mixed.. Soon all the servants were fast asleep. Shortly afterwards, the Kauravas set fire to the mansion. Soon the entire building was ablaze but not before the Pandavas made good their escape. Seeing the fire, people rushed to the spot. By that time, the building had been reduced to ashes.Believing the Pandavas to be dead, these people conveyed the news to Hastinapur. But then, the dead bodies charred inside the mansion were not those of the Pandavas. They were of the servants.

Duryodhana was absolutely delighted to hear that Pandavas died in the fire. But outwardly he put on a sad face and pretended to grieve over their death.

With utmost difficulty, the Pandavas crossed through the tunnel and entered the dense forest. With the exception of the powerful Bhima, all the others were exhausted. So he carried them through the forest and reached the Ganges where Vidura had arranged a boat for them. They crossed the river in total darkness and entered another mighty forest. From there, the Pandavas marched on, eating the forest produce and sleeping by turns. They were ever vigilant and ever confident that justice would be theirs sooner or later.

Hidimbi, a demoness, ruled over the forest where Pandavas had sought refuge. One day, while Bhima was fetching water for his mother and brothers, Hidimbi saw him and wanted to marry him. She herself proposed marriage to Bhima. But he was a human and she, a demoness. So, Hidimbi's

brother Hidimba objected to this marriage and challenged Bhima to a fight. Bhima lifted up the demon with his powerful arms and killed him by thrashing him on the ground. He then took Hidimbi to Kunthi. Kunthi agreed to this marriage and so, Bhima and Hidimbi were married. Hidimbi looked after the Pandavas well. She offered them good food and took care to see that they came to no harm in the forest. Subsequently she became pregnant. Bhima was very happy.

Meanwhile, the Pandavas reached the city of Ekachakra. But Hidimbi did not agree to go with them for she said, "I cannot bear to live outside the forest." Shortly afterwards, she gave birth to a son called Ghatotkacha.

In the city of Ekachakra, the Pandavas lived in the guise of Brahmins, begging for their food. They brought

home food and Kunthi always divided it into two portions - one portion for Bhima alone and the other portion for the rest of them. None could imagine or recognise them as the princes of Hastinapur!

One day, Kunthi heard her neighbour's wife cry. So she went to their house to find out the reason for such anguish. The neighbour's wife, with tears rolling down her cheeks said, "O! Great lady! You have been like a mother to us. But I do not know how you can help us, because this relates to a wicked Rakshasa by name Bakasura. Earlier, he used to pounce upon people and after killing them indiscriminately, would eat human flesh. To prevent such slaughter, the citizens of Ekachakra agreed to send a human - being to the demon daily, along with a cart load of rice and other delicacies. Tomorrow is

my turn and so, I have to send my only son to Bakasura. Only God can help us."

Kunthi pacified the woman and told her, "Don't worry, I will send one of my sons in the place of your son."

Bhima immediately agreed to go to Bakasura as his food. His aim was to kill the Rakshasa and provide peaceful living to the people of the city.

The next day Bhima drove the cart loaded with rice and other food straight

to the demon's cave. But even before he reached the cave, unable to bear his hunger, Bhima himself ate up all the food in the cart and gave out a loud belch. On hearing this, the demon, already angry that his food had been delayed, rushed out of his cave, only to find that the cart was empty. He charged towards Bhima to eat him up. Bhima just raised his fist and gave a severe blow to the demon. Then ensued a big fight between them but finally Bhima threw him down and smashed him to death. The Rakshasa howled so loudly in pain and hearing this, the people of the city trembled with fear, not knowing the outcome of this fight. But soon, their fear turned into joy when they saw Bhima dragging the body of the dead Bakasura. Little did they realise that this courageous man was none other than Bhima, one of the Pandava princes.

# Draupadi's Swayamvar

Draupadi was the daughter of Drupada, king of Panchala. Dhristadyumna was her brother. Drupada who had once been defeated by Arjun decided that a great warrior like him would be the best match for Draupadi. Drupada had earlier believed the Pandavas to be dead but had also heard rumours that they had escaped from the wax house. So, he hoped that Arjun would attend the Swayamvar.

Draupadi's Swayamvar had been arranged in the city of Kampilaya. Many princes had often dreamt about marrying this world renowned beautiful princess. News of the Swayamvar also reached the Pandavas. They decided to witness the Swayamvar along with the Brahmins going in groups to Kampilya.

The entire city of Kampilya had been decorated for the occasion with arches and festoons. There was a joyous and festive atmosphere. People put on their best clothes and excitedly talking about the royal wedding.

The marriage hall wore a magnificent look. In the midst of the hall, a big platform had been built and a huge vessel of water was placed at the centre. Right above the vessel was a revolving disc with a fish hooked to it. The prince aspiring to marry Draupadi had to string his bow and with it, shoot an arrow to hit the eye of the fish and that too, by looking at its reflection in the water kept below.

Drupada had purposely set up such an extremely difficult test for the archer for he knew that only a hero like Arjun would be able to accomplish the feat.

Many valiant princes had gathered there to prove their skill and win the hand of Draupadi.

Duryodhana, Karna, Jarasandha the king of Magadh, Shishupala, Shalya and many, many more able kings and princes were there. The Pandavas stood in a corner amidst a group of Brahmins.

At the auspicious moment, Draupadi, looking all the more dazzling as a bride-to-be, entered the hall. All the suitors were anxious. "Will Draupadi be mine?" was their thought. But was it so easy? Didn't they have to win the contest?

The kings and princes rose one after the other to string the bow. Some couldn't even lift it. Even if they could, one look at the rapidly revolving disc made them cross-eyed. They all gave it up. Then Karna stood up and walked

towards the dais. But Draupadi denied him the chance saying that she could not possibly marry the son of a charioteer. Feeling small, Karna returned to his seat. Finally, it looked as if Draupadi's Swayamvar would not take place at all.

Amidst the murmur of disappointment, stood up Arjun, seeking permission to contest. "How, could a Brahmin succeed when valiant princes have failed?" ridiculed the Kshatriyas. But impressed by Arjun's noble look, Drupada gave him the permission to contest. Arjun was delighted. He stringed the bow and concentrating on the reflection of the fish in the water, he aimed his arrow. The arrow directly hit the eye of the fish.

While the Brahmins and others shouted with joy and excitement, the defeated princes showed their anger on Drupada. "Why did you allow this? Can

a princess of Draupadi's stature marry
a poor Brahmin," was their ridicule.
Some threatened to kill Drupada. Some

protested loudly about being insulted. Amidst this confusion, Bhima and Yudhistira were afraid that someone might recognise them. Meanwhile Draupadi with love shining in her eyes for the valiant Arjun, garlanded him. Lord Krishna and his brother Balaram who had also graced the occasion, tried to pacify the princes but in vain. As the uproar continued Arjun and his brothers along with Draupadi quietly slipped out of the marriage hall. Seeing them departing, Drupada asked his son to follow them to know their true identity.

It was Arjun who had gained the hand of Draupadi and only he should have wed her. But destiny willed otherwise. The Pandavas returning to their abode, called out to their mother, "Mother, come and see our alms for to-day." And Kunthi also called out from inside the house, "Whatever you have

got, please share it among yourselves."
But when Kunthi actually saw
Draupadi, the enormity of what she
said, struck her. But she extended a
warm welcome to Draupadi.

Dhristadyumna who had followed
the Pandavas, closely observed them
and he was delighted at what he saw.
He returned to his father and told him
that the five Brahmins were none other
than the Pandavas and that Kunthi was
also with them. Drupada promptly
invited the Pandavas and Kunti to
Kampilya and on Kunthi's instructions,
gave his daughter in marriage to all the
five brothers. Lord Krishna and
Balaram witnessed the marriage.

Pandavas felt very happy at the out
come of events because they had the
support of Drupada and most important
of all, Krishna, the universal protector
was with them.

When news about Draupadi's Swayamvar reached Hastinapur, Duryodhana's hatred and jealousy knew no bounds. His bitter enemies, who, he thought, were burnt to ashes in Varanavati, were very much alive. To add to this, they were married to Draupadi and also gained the friendship of Drupada and Krishna.

Duryodhana found the situation unbearable. When he consulted Karna, his friend advised him to wage a war against the Pandavas, a conduct befitting a warrior. Duryodhana after taking the consent of his blind father, broached the topic with Bhishma, Drona and other elders but they did not support him on this. Instead, they advised him "Don't nurture any hatred towards your cousin brothers. It will only demean you. You will also lose the good-will of the people. Treat the Pandavas well. After all, they have not

done any injustice to you. Give them half the kingdom and end this enemity."

Neither Dhrithrashtra nor Duryodhana could go against the advice of Bhishma and Drona. So, reluctantly, they sent Vidura to the Pandavas to bring them back to Hastinapur.

Drupada had never liked Duryodhana. He knew of Duryodhana's plots to kill the Pandavas. He therefore objected to the Pandavas going back to Hastinapur but on Krishna's advice, agreed that they should claim their kingdom.

In the end, the Pandavas and Draupadi entered Hastinapur to a tumultuous welcome. People were overjoyed to see the Pandavas alive and also to have them as their rulers. Only the Kauravas found it unpalatable and were biding their time to avenge the Pandavas.

# The Rajasuya Yagna

**D**hrithrashtra totally ignored the Pandavas. He seemed to have forgotten that they were his brother's children. Their popularity and prosperity were unbearable to him. Hence, when he was forced into giving half the kingdom to the Pandavas, he deliberately allotted a barren and desolated land to them. Without grudging this offer, Yudhishtira accepted it and with his brothers, Draupadi and Kunthi, settled down in the place. Soon the Pandavas turned the barren land into a golden land. They built palaces and forts and also provided all the amenities fit for a great city. Thus a small place grew into a mighty capital called Indraprastha.

Soon, the people of the neighbouring places accepted Yudhishtira as their

king and several kings also sought his patronage by offering monetary tributes. In no time Yudhishtira's coffers were full. He therefore wanted to expand his kingdom. After all, he had the support of his valiant brothers.

At that time Yudhishtira's friends suggested that he conduct the Rajasuya Yagna so that he could become the emperor of a vast kingdom. But since they had to ensure whether there were other kings who could oppose him, Yudhishtira consulted his friend Krishna about this. Krishna told him that Magadha's king Jarasandha was the only king who was capable of challenging Yudhishtira's sovereignty. Hence, Jarasandha had to be defeated. Jarasandha was a wicked king. He had terrorized the entire world and Krishna wanted him to be annihilated. But Dharmaraja did not want to confront war with anybody.

After devoting a lot of thought, Yudhishtira, Krishna and other Pandavas went in disguise to see Jarasandha's capital Girivraja.

Jarasandha was born as two halves of a body. A lady named Jara, out of her capability had enjoined the two parts so that it became a baby and blessed him with immense power. Thus Jarasandha became very powerful. Krishna and the Pandavas in guise of being brahmins, participated in the Yagna that was taking place in Girivraj. But, Jarasandha's sharp eye noticed some scars and immediately realised that these ought to be war scars. He even identified Bhima. When Jarasandha demanded the truth of them, Pandavas replied frankly that they had come to seek combat with him. Undaunted, Jarasandha invited Bhima for a fight without weapons. Bhima and Jarasandha were so strong that they

fought for a fortnight without any signs of exhaustion. Even when Bhima managed to split Jarasandha's body into two halves, they would immediately adhere together and Lo! Jarasandha was ready for a fight.

Not knowing what to do, Bhima looked at Krishna for guidance and he saw Krishna tearing a straw into half and throwing them in totally opposite directions. Bhima took the hint and he tore Jarasandha into two halves and threw them so far away from each other that they could not come back together. Thus, Jarasandha died and Pandavas were victorious.

Pandavas freed all the princes who were imprisoned by Jarasandha and crowned his son as the king of Magadha. Now Yudhishtira could proclaim himself as the emperor of the entire world.

Yudhishtira made hectic preparations for the Rajasuya Yagna. He invited many kings for the event. Duryodhana, Karna, Bhishma, Drona, Shakuni the King of Gandhara, Sishupala, Krishna and several others accepted his invitation and reached Indraprastha to witness the Yagna.

On the ultimate day of the Yagna, Yudhishtira was to be proclaimed the emperor and a custom to render first honour to the guest who was considered most worthy among all others was to be followed. It was a huge congregation and Yudhishtira was of the opinion that Krishna should be honored first.

Sisupala the king of Chedi, hated Krishna and could not tolerate him. Laughing in derision he ridiculed Krishna of being a thief, of being the son of a cowherd and heaped many more insults on him. Unable to tolerate

Krishna being ridiculed, the elderly Bhishma stood up and revealed the secret behind Sisupala's birth.

Sisupala was Krishna's relative through his father Vasudeva. Sisupala was born ugly with three eyes and four arms and the royal astrologer had predicted that he would meet his death at the hands of the one who would cure him of his ugliness. Sisupala's mother roamed from town to town in search of a cure for her son's ugliness and in Dwaraka, Krishna touched the baby and the baby turned out to be a normal looking one. But, she was grieved to think that her son would die at the hands of Krishna. Krishna consoled her by saying, "Dear Aunt! I can condone one hundred mistakes of Sisupala, if he exceeds this limit, he is bound to die."

Enraged at Bhishma, Sisupala turned his ire towards Krishna and

ridiculed him further. Since his insults crossed the one hundred mark, Krishna stood up and used his Sudarshana Chakra towards Sisupala which chopped his head. He was thus slain.

Rajasuya Yagna was celebrated with a lot of pomp and pageantry and Yudhishtira was recognized as the emperor. The princes, priests, and other elders who had gathered for the occasion

praised the magnificence of the Yagna and returned to their places. Duryodhana burned with jealousy at the thought of Pandava's prosperity. His jealousy knew no bounds when he saw the artistically built palace with its crystal floors so exquisitely designed that it was difficult to differentiate between a fountain of water and a crystal floor. Duryodhana was so lost in his jealousy and mistaking the floor, he slipped on water and fell down. Draupadi who witnessed this scene from her balcony burst into uncontrollable laughter. Duryodhana was enraged, to say the least. He was all the more determined to punish the Pandavas by driving them out of Indraprastha by hook or by crook.

# The Gamble

Shakuni was the prince of Gandhara. Gandhari was his sister. Thus, Shakuni was Duryodhana's maternal uncle and was his constant companion in Hastinapur.

Shakuni was fully aware of Pandava's might and also knew of Duryodhana's intense hatred towards them. The evil minded Shakuni nurtured this hatred and advised Duryodhana to destroy the Pandava brothers. After the incident at Indraprastha, Shakuni went to the forlorn Duryodhana and told him, "My dear nephew! I know a way to drive the Pandavas out of Indraprastha, without any fight and without shedding any blood." Duryodhana's eyes lighted up in hope. He asked "Uncle, how is it possible?" Shakuni replied, "Yudhishtira

is very fond of the game of dice. You invite him for a game and I will play on your behalf. I will trick him into defeat and thus win his kingdom and his wealth for you. Do you like my plan?" Wouldn't Duryodhana be delighted at such an opportunity? But before sending a word to the Pandavas, Duryodhana and Shakuni went to Dhrithrashtra and explained their plan of inviting Yudhishtira for a game of dice, defeating him totally and taking away all his wealth and kingdom away from him. Dhrithrashtra at first did not favour the plan. But when Duryodhana insisted on this, Dhrithrashtra out of his blind love for his son relented. Ultimately, he summoned Vidura to invite Yudhishtira for the game of dice.

Yudhishtira had vowed that as an emperor he would never indulge in such games. But since his elderly uncle had

summoned him, he went to Hastinapur along with his brothers and the royal retinue.

Duryodhana had a magnificent hall specially erected for the game. Many distinguished persons of the Kuru clan, royal teachers and officials were present

in the hall on the day of the game and a huge platform had been erected. Shakuni invited Yudhishtira to the dais to start the game upon which

Yudhishtira asked Duryodhana as to who would play with him. Duryodhana replied that his uncle Shakuni would cast the dice instead of him. Yudhishtira was confident of defeating Duryodhana in a game of dice, but felt diffident against Shakuni as Shakuni was an expert player. So, he hesitated and said, "How could Shakuni play on your behalf when it is you who have invited me to this game?" Duryodhana looking deridingly asked "Well! Are you afraid of losing to my uncle." Yudhishtira flushed with embarrassment and said, "Duryodhana, I am not a coward, I shall play." The hall was full and everybody knew that the game would end in a bitter way, but they could do nothing about it. At first, gold, silver and ornaments were wagered and Yudhishtira lost them in no time. One by one he pledged his servants, his chariots, horses, armies

and lost them too. The fervent plea made by his brothers to stop the game did not have any effect on Yudhishtira. When he had nothing more to pledge he staked Sahadev and Nakul and Shakuni's cunning game made him lose them too. Shakuni taunted him by saying, "Yudhishtira, after all they are your step brothers, and that is why you could stake them. I bet you wouldn't dare offer Bhima and Arjun as stakes. Yudhishtira by that time was feeling thoroughly reckless and stung by Shakuni's retort continued the game by offering the ever victorious Arujun and Bhima as wagers. He lost them too. Shakuni then reminded Yudhishtira about Draupadi and said, "There is a very valuable jewel in your possession. I call upon you to continue the game with your wife Draupadi as wager." The desperated Yudhishtira pledged her too, and lost

her. Shakuni stood up in the assembly and shouted that he had won the Pandavas and Draupadi and they had to become his slaves. The entire gathering was stunned. Some wept with distress. Some blamed Duryodhana for the situation. Bhishma, Drona and Krupa were worried about the consequences.

Duryodhana roared like a lion, "Draupadi will henceforth be our maid. She is at our command." He turned towards Vidura and said "Vidura! Go and fetch her." Vidura exclaimed "Have you become insane? You are heading towards your own destruction." Duryodhana ignored Vidura's caution and sent a charioteer to fetch Draupadi. He was intent on humiliating Draupadi in full view of the gathering. Draupadi refused to go to the court of Duryodhana and said, "How could a man stake his

wife after he himself had lost the game. When I do not belong to him, how could he have the right to pledge me as a pawn? I refuse to come." Duryodhana was enraged on hearing this answer. "How dare the maid talks back like this? Duhshyasana, my brother! Bring that maid here, even if you have to drag her by the hair. This is my order."

Duhshyasana was wicked. He went quickly to Draupadi's chamber, caught her by her long black hair and dragged her to the assembly. Draupadi was extremely angry. She argued that she could not be staked as a pawn as Yudhishtira had lost his freedom to stake her much earlier. She appealed to the elders like Bhishma, Drona, Karna and Dhrithrashtra not to allow such a misdeed. Duryodhana had exceeded the limits of decency. Totally ignoring what was right and what was wrong, and also

ignoring that the assembly consisted of male members and the elders, Duryodhana instructed Duhshyasana to seize Draupadi's garments and disrobe her. The gathering was aghast. How could anybody tolerate a lady being thus insulted? Even Dhrithrashtra had not anticipated that the matter would be carried out so far. He begged his son, "Oh! My dear son, do not resort to such acts and bring disrepute to the Kaurava's clan." Bhishma and Drona were full of grief that they had to witness such a scene. But, Duryodhana was adamant. He ordered his brother to pull out Draupadi's sari. The helpless Draupadi trembled with fear like a poor fawn stricken by a tiger. None among the gathering could protect her. Her five husbands who were described as the mighty ones were now Kaurava's slaves. At that moment, she could only think of

Divine Intervention and prayed to Lord Krishna to come to her help. As Duhshyasana tried to disrobe Draupadi, another garment would appear on her and soon a heap of garments were piled up in the assembly.

Duhshyasana pulled and pulled her garments and there seemed to be no end to them. He was so tired that he had to give up. While the assembly watched this miracle, the frustrated Duryodhana walked out of the assembly.

Draupadi slowly opened her eyes. The Pandavas stood in one corner bowing their heads in shame. It was Bhima who broke the deathly silence. He swore, "Sooner or later I shall rend the breast and drink the blood of Duhshyasana". Draupadi also swore that till Duhshyasana was killed, she would not tie up her hair. Nature also seemed to protest against such a

shameful act. Suddenly the earth seemed to quiver. There were several evil omens. Rain also poured out of its fury.

Dhrithrashtra called Draupadi to his side and attempted to soothe her by saying, "Child, My son has erred. Whatever you want, I will grant to you as an atonement for his mistakes". Draupadi a devout wife, wanted her husbands to be freed from bondage, she also asked for return of the weapons. Dhrithrashtra was even prepared to give back Indraprastha to them. But, self respect would not make Draupadi to accept the kingdom from her enemies. She refused this offer.

The Pandavas left the cursed hall stunned by the turn of events. Draupadi followed them.

Duryodhana was extremely angry

when he heard that his blind father had returned all the weapons to the Pandavas and freed them from bondage. He showed his anger on his father. The poor Dhrithrashtra did not even have the courage to stop his son's shouting. Finally, Duryodhana pressurised Dhrithrashtra to call Yudhishtira once again for the game of dice and that whoever was the loser was to go on exile to the forest for twelve years and spend the thirteenth year incognito. If they were to be recognised in the thirteenth year, they were to go into exile for another twelve years. The elders tried their level best to make Duryodhana come to his senses and not to bring any more misfortune to the Pandavas. How could Duryodhana agree when he didn't want them alive. His sole intention was to banish them forever.

Yudhistira too could not resist the temptation of playing the game and win back what he had lost. So, he returned to Hastinapur and sat again for the game of dice. Needless to say, Yudhishtira lost again and had to leave for the forest.

When they set out for the forest, the citizens of Hastinapur requested them not to go. Their grief and lamentation filled the sky. When Dhrithrashtra learnt about their departure, he was filled with even more fear and anxiety. But Duryodhana was not moved. Bhishma and Drona could not even utter a word because they were under the obligation of Dhrithrashtra.

When Krishna came to know of the incident, he went to Hastinapur and fetched his sister Subhadra who was Arjun's wife and her young son Abhimanyu to Dwaraka. When

Draupadi's brother Dhristadyumna heard of Draupadi's humiliation, he vowed to take revenge against the Kauravas. Kunthi stayed with Vidura.

## The Exile

To be in exile in a forest is a very tough experience, because a forest is full of wild animals. It is an area where Rakshasaas roam about freely. Mostly it is dark in the forest. One has to go in search of water and live on tubers and fruits. The Pandavas who had always lived in a royal style had to face all such hardships in the forest. But their courage and their righteousness never failed them.

Yudhishtira alongwith his brothers and wife lived in a forest called Kamyaka. Not many people lived there. Only a few sages could be found and

living in a forest was really very tough. All such hardships constantly reminded them about Duryodhana's treachery. They could never forget that their hard earned kingdom was lost to Duryodhana in a deceitful game and neither could they forgive him for his treatment towards Draupadi. So they always sought ways and means to get back their kingdom.

Within a short time the Pandavas moved on to another forest. Meantime, Yudhishtira felt that the only way they could get back their kingdom was to wage a war with Duryodhana. For this purpose they had to secure necessary weapons and collect an army for which they had to contact kings friendly to them.

Wicked people always remain wicked. They take great delight in harassing good people. Duryodhana

after banishing the Pandavas was afraid that they would reclaim their kingdom once their exile was over. That is why he wanted to have them killed during the exile itself. Hence he counselled with Shakuni and Karna who were close to him and said, "Pandavas should now be weak without proper food and without proper weapons. It will be so easy to defeat them now." Shakuni and Karna agreed that it could be so. But, they needed the permission of the elders to put this plan into action. So, Duryodhana thought of an idea. Under the pretext of counting the cattle head he invaded various woods and forests. When he entered the forest where Pandavas had sought refuge, Chitrasena, a Gandharva king, under instructions from Indra, waylaid Duryodhana and his army and defeated him. Shakuni and Karna fled from the

place while Chitrasena dragged Duryodhana to Yudhishtira. Yudhishtira was a very righteous man. He always looked upon Duryodhana as one of his brothers. So, he ordered Duryodhana's release. Feeling insulted at his failure, Duryodhana returned to Hastinapur nursing his wounds and waiting for the right time to avenge defeat on the Pandavas.

During their exile in the forest, the Pandavas met several sages and always sought the righteous path from them. While in exile, Bhima met his elder brother Hanuman. Arjun observed penance in the Himalayas and pleased with him, Eswar, Yama, Kubera, Varuna and others granted him several very powerful weapons. Arjun also learnt dance and music from Chitrasena.

The exile period of the Pandavas was

drawing to a close. One day a Brahmin came running to Yudhishtira and requested him to get him back the deer skin which had got entangled in a deer's horn. The Pandavas went in search of the deer but found it difficult to catch it. They were feeling thirsty after the chase and hence Yudhishtira asked his younger brother Sahadeva to fetch water from a nearby lake.

Sahadeva did not return even after a long time. The worried Yudhishtira sent Nakul after him. Nakul also did not return. Then he sent Bhima. But he too didn't return. Arjun also followed suit. So, Yudhishtira himself went in search of his brothers. After walking through a long distance, he saw a crystal clear lake. Lotus flowers had bloomed beautifully in the lake and presented a delightful scene. So, he thought that his brothers would be somewhere around,

admiring the scenery. But when he looked around, he was shocked to see his very dear brothers dead by the banks of the lake. Yudhishtira could not believe his own eyes. How could this happen, he wondered. Tears welled up in his eyes at the thought that his brothers were no longer alive. Actually, when the brothers went one by one to fetch water from the lake, an Yaksha had laid a condition that they could not fetch water till they could answer his. questions. But the thirsty brothers ignored him, drank the water and fell unconscious. Yudhishtira was not aware of this. He too could not contain his thirst. When he approached the lake to drink water, he heard a voice. It belonged to this Yaksha.

"Answer my questions before drinking the water!" said the voice.

Without losing his cool, Yudhishtira replied, "You can ask me anything you

want, I will answer them to the best of my ability.

"Which has the fastest speed?"

"Speed of the mind."

"What is superior to earth?"

"Mother."

"What gives happiness to man?"

"To give up anger."

"How can one be the richest?"

"By giving up desire."

"What causes man's destruction?"

"His haughtiness."

"What weapon do you need to face danger?"

"Bravery."

The Yaksha had many more such questions to ask and when Yudhishtira answered them promptly, he was highly pleased.

"I can make one of your brothers alive, but who should it be?" said the Yaksha. Yudhishtira loved all his brothers equally. But without hesitating, he said, "My brother Nakul." Yaksha was surprised. "Instead of Bhima or Arjun, why do you ask for Nakul's life?"

Yudhishtira said in a calm voice, "Sir, I agree that Bhima and Arjun are my brothers. Nakul is my step mother Madri's son. I cannot sacrifice him for the sake of my own brothers."

Appreciating Yudhishtira's attitude the Yaksha brought back Nakul to life. "I will put back life to another brother of yours. Who should it be", he asked. Yudhishtira asked for Sahadev. Astonished, the Yaksha said, "Yudhishtira, at least now you could have asked for one of your valiant brothers." Yudhishtira had an apt reply,

"Sir, when my father died, my mother Madri also gave up her life. But she ordained me to look after Nakul and Sahadev as my own children. How could I fail her?"

Extremely pleased with Yudhishtira the Yaksha brought back Bhima and Arjun back to life and blessed all of them well. The Yaksha was none other than Yama, father of Yuddhishtira. He blessed his own son by saying. "Your exile ends now. One more year in incognito and your hardships will be over. So, you go to Matsya Kingdom and live there in disguise under King Virata."

The Pandavas along with Draupadi began their journey to Matsya Kingdom.

## The Slaying of Kichaka

As per the condition laid down during the wager, the Pandavas

completed twelve years of exile in the forest. They now had to live incognito for one year. During the year if their true identity was to be found out, they were to spend another twelve years in exile.

The Pandavas followed the Yaksha's instructions and entered the city of Matsya in disguise. Prior to that, they wrapped all their weapons in a gunny bag and hung it to a branch of a tree in a crematorium which was outside the city. Yudhishtira secured the friendship of king Virata, under the name of Kankabhatta. Bhima was employed as a cook in the royal kitchen and was known as Valala. Arjun, who had learnt the art of dance and music under Chitrasena, called himself as Brihannala, and dressing up like a woman taught these arts to the king's children. Sahadev obtained employment in the cowshed and Nakul

in the stables. Draupadi worked as a maid to the queen under the name of Sairandri. It grieved Yudhishtira that all of them had to do menial tasks, especially Draupadi.

The queen had a brother called Kichaka. He was the commander-in-chief of Virata and wielded a lot of power and influence.

Once Kichaka went to the queen's chamber to meet his sister and saw Draupadi there. Draupadi was extremely beautiful and Kichaka was so smitten by her beauty that he talked indecently to her. Scared of his intentions. Draupadi escaped from his clutches and fled to her own room.

Kichaka who had great influence over his sister, went to her and told her about his passion for the maid. "Dear brother!" Sudeshna, the queen, advised him, "Do not force any woman into

submission. Give up your desire for her". But Kichaka would not listen. He persuaded his sister by saying, "After all, she is just a maid. Make her come to my chamber." Out of her love for her brother, the queen decided upon a plan.

That evening Sudeshna summoned Draupadi and instructed her to carry a jug of intoxicating drink to Kichaka. Draupadi hesitated but she had to follow the queen's orders. She went to the royal quarters of Kichaka and left the wine jug at the doorstep. She then hurriedly tried to get away from the place but Kichaka chased her. Trembling like a leaf, Draupadi fled to the court of Virata, fell at the feet of Yudhishtira who was in the midst of a game with the king, and begged him to come to her rescue. By that time, Kichaka reached the court and kicked her in the presence of all. Though Yudhishtira was pained to see this, he

did not utter a single word, for he could not possibly reveal his relationship with Sairandri (Draupadi) and suffer another twelve years of exile. So he kept quiet. Crying over her helplessness Draupadi returned to her room. That very night she went to the royal kitchen, woke up Bhima and told him about Kichaka. "Either you kill Kichaka, or I will kill myself," threatened Draupadi in desperation. The enraged Bhima assured Draupadi that he would kill Kichaka. But not wanting to act in haste and reveal his true identity, Bhima advised Draupadi to entice Kichaka to the dancing hall the next night and that he would take care of the rest.

Draupadi visited Kichaka the next morning and pretending to yield to his desires, invited him to come alone to the dancing hall that night. The excited Kichaka waited for nightfall.

That night, Kichaka drank plenty of wine, dressed himself well and went to the dancing hall. In the dim light, he saw someone lying on a cot with a saree covered over the face. Thinking that this was Sairandri, he gently laid his hands on that form. Bhima who was on the cot draped in a saree, leapt upon Kichaka like a thunder, thrashed him into a lump and killed him. He then quietly slipped

out of the hall and went to sleep on the kitchen floor.

In the morning the news about Kichaka's death spread like fire all over the city. Sudeshna was filled with grief about her brother's death. She suspected Sairandri about this but had no proof.

The people of Virata were stunned that the valiant Kichaka met with such a terrible death. They felt that the person who killed Kichaka ought to be much more powerful than Kichaka himself. But none had the tiniest inkling that it was Bhima who killed Kichaka.

## To the defense of Virata

When Duryodhana heard about the mysterious way in which Kichaka was killed, he guessed that Bhima could have killed Kichaka,

because it was a well known fact that only Bhima was as strong as Kichaka. So, Duryodhana surmised that the Pandavas were living under a different identity in the kingdom of Matsya. Moreover, word had reached Duryodhana that Sudeshna had a maid Sairandri who claimed that she had five Gandharvas as her husbands. There was no further doubt about the Pandavas being in the kingdom of Matsya.

"Kichaka's death will have weakened the Virata king. If we were to attack him now and if the Pandavas are really hiding there, they will definitely come out to fight to repay for his hospitality. We will thus have tracked them down and can banish them to the forest again, thought Duryodhana. When he put forward this idea to Karna and others, they too agreed. Susharma, king of Trigarth was Duryodhana's friend and

hence he agreed to invade Matsya by seizing the cattle and by destroying the gardens and fields on the way. Duryodhana was to launch his attack from the northern side.

Virata was yet to get over the loss of Kichaka and hence he was in no condition to face a war with the neighbouring kingdom. When he discussed his plight with Kanka, that is Yudhishtira, the latter said, "O King, there is no time to waste. You summon the army and I will help you out. Similarly Valala, the cook Dharmagranthi in the stable and Tantripala were earlier employed in the army of the Pandavas and so, given an opportunity, they will prove their skill in warfare." Virata was too glad to have help.

Bhima, Nakul and Sahadev were happy to prove their worth and in no

time defeated Susharma's army. Virata was delighted with the victory.

Meanwhile, the Kauravas had rounded up the cows in the north and the cowherds ran to the palace to seek help. In the absence of Virata, they met Uttara Kumar, his son. Uttara boasted to them about his valour and also that he could defeat the Kauravas and recover the cows single-handed if only he could get a charioteer to take him to the battlefield. Sairandri who overheard this conversation suggested to him, "O Prince! Take Brihannala with you. She will be a very good charioteer."

Uttarkumar doubted whether a female could be a charioteer but since he did not have the courage to go alone, he agreed to the suggestion and took Brihannala (Arjun in disguise) to the war front. But there the sight of a big army, the sight of the wounded soldiers

and the sound of clashing weapons unnerved the prince. Trembling with fear, he wanted to go back to the safety of his palace. But Arjun, in the disguise of Brihannala, encouraged Uttarkumar to fight like a brave person, "You have to fight to protect your land," he told the prince, "otherwise, the enemy will destroy all of us. Do not fear; I am with you."

Arjun took Uttarkumar to the tree in the crematorium where the Pandavas had hid their weapons. He asked the prince to bring down the weapons from the tree, which, he said belonged to the Pandavas. The prince who no longer felt any cowardice, brought down the gleaming weapons from the tree. He felt that Brihannala was no ordinary person. He wanted to know her true identity. When Brihannala told him that she was Arjun. Uttara folded his hands in

reverence. "Please forgive me for treating you - a valiant hero, as a charioteer," he said in a humble tone.

Arjun advised him about behaving like a warrior and together they hastened towards the battlefield.

When Duryodhana saw Uttarkumar approaching the battlefield with a female charioteer, he felt that victory was undoubtedly very easy. Arjun observed from a distance Bhishma, Drona and Kripacharya standing along with Karna and Duryodhana in the battlefield. He stringed his bow and used three arrows. One arrow fell at the feet of Bhishma, the other at Drona's and the third at Kripa's feet. This salutation made all of them exclaim, "Arjun is here." On hearing this, Duryodhana immediately cried aloud, "Arjun has been identified before the exile period is over. The Pandavas should undergo twelve more years of exile." But Drona clarified and said, "The stipulated period ended just before

we recognised Arjun as the charioteer."
There was an argument over this
between Drona, Duryodhana and
Drona's son Ashwathama. Finally
Bhishma put an end to this war of words
by reminding them that they had to
urgently confront Arjun.

Arjun and Uttarkumar fought
valiantly and defeated the Kaurava
army. Duryodhana fled from the
battlefield leaving behind the stolen
cattle. The entire army retreated to
Hastinapur.

Virata who was overjoyed to hear
about this victory against the Kauravas
arranged a grand welcome to his son,
Uttara. But he did not realise that a
youngster like Uttara could not have
defeated war veterans like Bhishma and
Drona. He was so full of praise for his
son. So, when Yudhishtira revealed the
truth that Brihannala was the true

reason for winning the war, Virata was annoyed that Kanka equated Uttara with a mere woman. In a fit of anger, Virata flung the dice he was playing on Kanka's face. Kanka was hurt and blood oozed from his face. Immediately Sairandri hastened to his side, wiped the blood with a cloth and squeezed it into a cup. Virata was further enraged. He shouted at Sairandri, "Why are you concerned about a total stranger?" he asked her.

"Kanka is not his true name," replied Sairandri. "He is a king and it does not augur well for your kingdom if his blood drops on the floor." Virata was very confused with this reply.

Right at that moment, Uttarkumar entered the palace and revealed to his father, the identity of Brihannala, Kanka, Sairandri, Bhima, Nakul and Sahadev. Virata was aghast at the thought that he had treated the mighty

Pandavas as servants and that Draupadi worked as a maid to the queen. The queen sought Draupadi's forgiveness.

Virata, in gratitude to the Pandavas for defending the kingdom, gave his daughter, Princess Uttara, in marriage to Arjun's son Abhimanyu in the presence of Krishna, Balaram and Drupada.

The exile and the incognito life of the Pandavas came to an end. What would be their next action? Was the thought foremost in everybody's mind. Some suggested to the Pandavas to defeat the Kauravas through a war and win back their kingdom. But war meant bloodshed and loss of lives. Hence Krishna advised the Pandavas to avoid a war. "But don't be cowards," he counselled, "If a peaceful settlement between you and the Kuravas cannot be reached, let us wage a war. But before

that, let us try to reach a compromise with them." Krishna wanted to avoid war, though he knew that Duryodhana would never listen to any reason. Krishna also knew that a war was inevitable between the Pandavas and the Kauravas.

## Krishna's Mediation

Duryodhana was a very adamant person. He could never concede anything at all. The messenger sent by the Pandavas through Drupada, read out before Duryodhana his various misdeeds against the Pandavas and called upon him to return their kingdom. The messenger also warned Duryodhana of the consequences of war if he did not agree for a peaceful settlement. Duryodhana was enraged to receive such a message. The elderly Bhishma who was present in the court,

advised Duryodhana to honourably give back Pandava's share of the kingdom. Otherwise the Kauravas would all be destroyed, he warned. Karna scorned Bhishma for siding the Pandavas. "They have foolishly lost their kingdom. Why should we return it," was his argument.

Dhrithrashtra sent an appeal to the Pandavas through Sanjay that they should give up their claim over the kingdom and avert a war. Pandavas were temporarily staying near Virata city of Matsya land. When Sanjay tried to convince Yudhishtira to give up any claim over the kingdom, Yudhishtira politely refused, "I have been made a king once and hence cannot live like a beggar. We Pandavas are not greedy. We are only asking for our share of the kingdom. If Duryodhana opposes this, at least give us five villages, one for each of us. We shall be content with this offer

and shall not wage a war," he said.

When Sanjay conveyed this message to Dhrithrashtra and his sons, Duryodhana laughed. The mighty Pandavas, with all their talk of dignity, asking for a mere five villages amused him. But his father found sense in this told him, "Son! I am sure you can give away the five villages. The rest of the empire will be yours." Duryodhana flatly refused by saying, "Dear father, I shall not part with even a needle-point of land," and walked out of the meeting.

Duryodhana just did not want to listen to any good advice or to reason. He was obsessed with destroying the Pandavas totally. Karna, Shakuni, Dushyasana and others encouraged him in this. Elders like Bhishma, Drona and Kripa were totally ignored. The blind Dhrithrashtra was like a puppet in his son's hands.

Duryodhana's proclamation that he would not give even a needle-point of land to the Pandavas dismayed Krishna. He felt that there was no more scope for peace talks but as a final effort, decided to personally go to Hastinapur and negotiate with the Kauravas. Draupadi did not favour this. The wicked ones ought to be punished was her attitude. She told her five husbands, "If you do not want to wage a war, I will seek the help of my father, the king of Drupada and Dhrishtadyumna, my brother. I have five sons to go to the battlefield." She could not forget the utter humiliation she faced at the hands of the Kauravas at a full gathering. Krishna consoled her by saying, "Dear sister, Duryodhana will never agree to a peaceful settlement and hence the final outcome will be a war. But I will have to make a last attempt." So saying, he departed for Hastinapur.

Duryodhana wanted to accord a grand welcome to Krishna. But instead of going straight to the court of the Kauravas, Krishna spent some time at Vidura's house and then went to the court, where Bhishma, Drona, Dhrithrashtra and Vidura were present. Duryodhana warmly welcomed Krishna and offered him a jewel-studded throne. "Krishna, it was below your dignity to stay with low-born Vidura. You should have accepted my hospitality," chided Duryodhana. Vidura, hurt by Duryodhana's cruel words refused to co-operate with him any further. Duryodhana, at that moment, did not realise what a loss this would be.

Krishna rose from his seat and facing the king, explained his intention to avert a war between the Kauravas and the Pandavas. "Dhrithrashtra, please treat the Pandavas honourably and

return their share of the kingdom. Do not cause destruction to the Kuru clan," Krishna said.

Dhrithrashtra pleaded his helplessness and so Krishna turned his attention towards Duryodhana and said gently, "Duryodhana, please be reasonable. If not half the kingdom at least five villages will make the Pandavas happy." Duryodhana stuck to his word, said a firm 'No' and walked out of the court.

Krishna pleaded with the elders about the senseless attitude of Duryodhana. "It is better to do away with one Duryodhana to save the other Kauravas," was Krishna's better advice to the others.

"Krishna on the pretence of mediation, is plotting to kill me," accused Duryodhana when he heard

about this advice. He immediately ordered his brother Duhshyasana to seize Krishna with ropes.

How is it possible to tie down the Protector of the Universe, the Omnipotent Krishna? When Duryodhana and his brothers rushed back to the palace court to imprison Krishna. Krishna revealed his Viswarupa. Wherever Duryodhana and Duhshyasana turned, they saw only Krishna, there was Krishna on every seat and on every throne. Who was the real Krishna?

Krishna's Viswarupa was the magnificent revelation of the Supreme Being. Even the blind Dhrithrashtra temporarily regained his eyesight and was able to see the Vishwarupa. While all the others were stupefied by this revelation, the ignorant Duryodhana termed it as a magic trick of Krishna.

When Duryodhana reiterated his obstinacy, Krishna left the court after resuming his normal form.

He went straight to Kunthi and told her about the events of the day. She was extremely distressed to learn that her sons had to resort to war. When she thought of Karna, her heart felt heavy. She wanted to reveal the secret about Karna's birth, in the hope that once he learnt the truth, he would not fight against his own brothers. Krishna also agreed with her, but suggested that she should make Karna promise her that he would not use the same arrow twice in the war.

Mother and son were to come face to face at last.

Kunthi knew that Karna offered his prayers to the Sun God every morning by the side of the river. So she waited

for him till his prayers were over. When he turned back, he saw Kunthi. He touched her feet in reverence. In a trembling voice, Kunthi addressed Karna as "Son!" Karna felt that she wanted to say something important to him.

"Son! you have always believed yourself to be Adiratha's son. This is not the truth. You were born a Kshatriya and you were born to me." So saying, she could no longer control her emotions and wept bitterly. She then told him about his birth and about setting him afloat in the river. She wanted to be forgiven for her action.

On hearing the truth about his birth, Karna said sadly, "Mother, you have got me into a predicament by revealing the truth. I can only say that fate has been very cruel to me."

Kunthi touched him gently and

continued to say, "Child! You are my eldest born. The Pandavas are your younger brothers. Not knowing the truth, you have joined hands with Duryodhana. But it is never too late. Come back to us and be a king. I assure you that you will have the abiding loyalty of your younger brothers."

Karna was a true friend of Duryodhana. He was ever grateful to his friend for his large-heartedness in crowning him as the king of Anga. So he told Kunthi in a firm voice, "Mother! I cannot give up my friendship for the sake of a throne. Duryodhana has total confidence in me. I cannot betray him at this moment."

"Son! You have no consideration for your poor mother?" asked Kunthi. Though Karna did not offer any reply, he could not forget the humiliation he had suffered in his entire life as being

the son of a charioteer. Neither Kunthi nor the Pandavas could wipe out his unpleasant memories.

"Please forgive me," said Karna to Kunthi, "I promise you that I shall not fight against Yudhishtira, Bhima, Nakul or Sahadev. But I shall not spare Arjun. I will not hesitate even to kill him. If he were to die at my hands, you still will have five sons. If I were to be killed by Arjun, you will still have five sons."

Kunthi then took courage and told Karna, "Son! You speak like a true Kshatriya. But promise me that you shall not use the same arrow twice on Arjun." The ever-generous Karna agreed to this and Kunthi returned home with a heavy heart.

Karna walked towards the palace with mixed emotions.

Such is the path of destiny!

# Kurukshetra

There was no doubt in everybody's mind that war was inevitable. Many people felt that cousins ought not resort to war, fighting over land. Others were of the opinion that Duryodhana ought not have been so adamant. The fact that Lord Krishna had himself tried to mediate between the hostile cousins and had failed disillusioned many. When Krishna returned from Hastinapur and informed Yudhishtira about the outcome of his trip, he felt very sad. The peace loving Yudhishtira lamented that bloodshed could not be stopped. Krishna returned to Dwaraka.

Drupada and Krishna were the only friends the Pandavas had. Drupada was waiting for an opportunity to avenge his daughter's humiliation. He was ready to

lend his army to Dharmaraja. Krishna's army consisted of Yadavas. Duryodhana wanted to avail of this army's services. Moreover he knew that Krishna's support was of utmost importance. So he went to Dwaraka to meet Krishna. Meanwhile, Arjun also reached Dwaraka to seek Krishna's help for Yudhishtira. Krishna who knew of these intentions, pretended to be fast asleep as soon as Duryodhana and Arjun reached his doorstep. Duryodhana, befitting the status of a king, preferred to sit on the seat placed near Krishna's head. He waited for Krishna to wake up. Arjun sat on a stool near Krishna's feet. As soon as Krishna opened his eyes, he saw Arjun first. Naturally, he could not have noticed Duryodhana first as he was sitting near the head. And naturally, Krishna talked to Arjun first. Duryodhana could not tolerate this and so he emitted a sound to catch Krishna's

attention. Immediately Krishna turned towards him and exclaimed, "Oh Duryodhana! You are also here. This is an honour for me. What can I do for you?

Duryodhana replied, "Yashoda-nandan, I have come to seek your help in the forthcoming war. Undoubtedly, victory will be mine. Hence, please be with us." Arjun also said, "Krishna, I am also here to ask for your help. We will be honoured to have you with us."

Krishna was in a dilemma. Both of them were his relatives and hence he ought to extend help to both of them. So he told them, "Dear Duryodhana and dear Arjun, both of you are my relatives. If I come to your help, my army will also assist you. But I will not personally take up arms. Nor will I participate in the actual fighting. So you have an option. One of you can take my entire army and

the other could have me. But since I spoke to Arjun first, he will have the first privilege."

The Pandavas were aware of Krishna's divinity. So Arjun at once said, "Krishna, I do not want your army. We want only you with us." Duryodhana was relieved to hear this. After all, Krishna had already said that he himself would not fight. So, what was the use of having him? he cried out in delight, "Krishna, in that case, give me your army." Krishna agreed to both these requests.

The war fever gripped one and all. The Pandavas and the Kauravas reviewed their respective armies to assess their strength. Duryodhana had a sister by name Dushyale. Her husband was Jayadrata, the Saindhava king. So, Duryodhana had his backing. Shalya, the king of Madra also was with the Kauravas. Susharma, the king of

Trigarth and his children had always extended their help to Duryodhana. The Yadava army sent by Krishna also swelled Duryodhana's strength. Bhishma, Drona, Kripa and Ashwathama were already with the Kauravas. Thus, the Kaurava's army numbered eleven Akshohinis*.

The Pandavas had the support of Drupada, Dhrishtadyumna, Amba who was born as Shikandi to Drupada in order to settle scores with Bhishma, Virata, Satyaki and others. Bhima and Arjun, themselves were very valiant. Abhimanyu, the fourteen years old, son of Arjun and Subhadra also announced that he was taking part in the war. Bhima's son Ghatotkacha was also there. The Pandavas in all, had seven

---

* One Akshohini = A battalion consisting of 21,870 elephants; 21,870 chariots; 65,610 horses and an infantry of 1,09,350.

Akshohinis. Yudhishtira divided these into seven divisions and appointed a commander-in-chief for each one of them. Bhima headed one such division. Since Krishna did not wish to wage the war, he told Arjun that he would be his charioteer.

Duryodhana also made hectic preparations to appoint commanders-in-chief for his army. The elderly Bhishma, a great warrior, was appointed as the Supreme - General in charge over all the other chiefs. Karna, who always felt that Bhishma had a soft corner for the Pandavas, was annoyed by this appointment, He wanted the post for himself. He therefore refused to take up arms till Bhishma was continued as the Supreme General. This infighting saddened Duryodhana. But he could not snatch away the post from a person of Bhishma's stature.

Bhishma, the father figure of the Kuru clan announced the commencement of the Kurukshetra war.

The Kaurava army and the Pandava army faced each other in the battlefield of Kurukshetra.

Sri Krishna entered the battlefield as Arjun's charioteer. The Hanumadhwaja (flag showing Hanuman) fluttered atop the chariot. Krishna blew the Panchajanya conch and Arjun blew the Devadatta conch to indicate the war.

The beating of war-drums, the neighing of the horses and the trumpet-like sound of the elephants filled Arjun with the excitement of war. But as he neared the Kaurava army, he saw the grand old man Bhishma, he saw his Gurus- Drona and Kripa and he saw his cousin brothers and other relatives. All

of them were dear to him. All of them were the revered ones.

Arjun hesitatingly asked Krishna. "Should I kill my own kith and kin for my selfishness? Should I kill my own friends just to gain victory over them? I am unable to do it." So saying he quickly put down his weapons.

To remove this deep agitation in Arjun's mind, Krishna spoke to him softly, "Arjun, war is inevitable. This

may seem to be a cruel, unjust way to you. But have you forgotten the grave injustice meted out by the Kauravas? Such a conflict arises between human beings upon this world. Who are you to kill? Who are they to be killed. It is God's will. We are only empowered to carry out our duties assigned to each of us."

Krishna further explained the various means of attaining God. He preached Arjun about the path of devotion and the path of duty. To fight for justice is duty. "Do your duty without desiring for reward or for fame," was the gospel of Sri Krishna. This is known as the **Bhagavad Gita**, hailed as the treasure of knowledge for the entire mankind.

Lord Krishna then exhibited his Vishwarupa and said, "I am the beginning and the end of all beings upon this world. I am Omnipresent and

Omnipotent. Without my being, nothing lives. I am present in the plant, in the tree, in the atmosphere, in the sky and everything else upon the earth. I protect those who believe in me. O! Arjun! Hence give up the doubts that haunt you, pick up the weapons and fight."

Listening to the *Gitopadesh* (Preaching of Gita), a new light of knowledge dawned upon Arjun. "The Supreme Being is the puppeteer and we are mere puppets in his hands. It is now my duty to fight and this is the path of duty"- thus Arjun readied himself for the war.

The Kurukshetra war waged for eighteen days. During these days, a lot of blood was shed. Each day witnessed the death of thousands of soldiers, horses and elephants. From dawn to dusk, the war went on. It provided ample opportunity to the soldiers and

to the commanders to prove their worth. Every evening at sunset, a bugle was blown to indicate the end of the day's battle. And each night, the losses in terms of men and animals were reviewed and the next day's plan of action finalised.

Bhishma alone waged the war for ten days. Abhimanyu faced Bhishma the first day of the war but had to concede defeat at the hands of Bhishma. Virata's children who came to the help of Abhimanyu were killed.

Arjun would make up his mind each day that he would kill Bhishma but did not have the heart to kill the grand old man who was a father-figure to all of them. Bhishma's attacks were so devastating that it looked as if a ball of fire was engulfing the enemies. Because of Bhishma, the death toll in the Pandava camp was very high. Hence

Krishna often urged Arjun to kill Bhishma but seeing Arjun's hesitancy in doing so, on the ninth day of the war, Krishna jumped out of the chariot with the intention of fighting with Bhishma. But Arjun reminded him about his decision on not taking part in the war directly. Arjun promised Krishna that Bhishma would be slain the next day.

It was neither easy nor possible to kill Bhishma. The tenth-day of the Kurukshetra war dawned. At the instance of Krishna, Arjun made Shikandi, the daughter of Drupada stand in front of him. He then attacked Bhishma. Upon which, Bhishma did not wish to fight against a woman and decided to lay down his weapons. As he could command his own death, he also decided to welcome death. So he purposely did not retaliate against Arjun's arrows. With arrows sticking all

over his body. Bhishma pitamah fell down. But his body could not touch the ground because of the numerous arrows sticking out. It was thus a bed of arrows for Bhishma.

The battlefield suddenly was quiet. A ceasefire was announced. The Pandavas and the Kauravas rushed to the side of Bhishma. Duryodhana tried to place a pillow under Bhishma's head but the great man refused. He wanted a pillow befitting a warrior. Arjun understood what he meant and created a support for Bhishma's head by striking three arrows on the ground under the head. Even at that moment, Bhishma advised Duryodhana to make peace with the Pandavas. But Duryodhana refused yet again.

Bhishma felt very thirsty. At once Arjun shot an arrow into the earth. Pure water gushed out from the hole and like

a fountain, reached Bhishma's lips gently. It looked as if Bhishma's mother Ganga had surfaced from the ground to bid farewell to her noble son. Bhishma then said, "I will lie here till the sun travels northwards. My soul will then depart." His body thus lay in the battlefield. The day's fighting was over. Duryodhana returned to his camp to decide upon the new Supreme-Commander in the place of Bhishma. The loss of Bhishma was a great setback to Duryodhana.

Karna was appointed as the Supreme - Commander for the eleventh day of the war. But Karna, out of respect for Drona, gave up the position in his favour. The eleventh day of the war dawned. Bugles were sounded and conches were blown. Duryodhana had instructed Drona that he should imprison Yudhishtira as the day's

trophy. He intended to banish the Pandavas to the forest forever. Drona reluctantly agreed to this task as he felt obligated to the Kauravas.

When Drona launched a direct attack on Yudhishtira, Arjun tried to move closer to his brother but was stopped by Susharma's children who also fought bravely. Like a ray of lightning, Arjun was at the side of Yudhishtira one moment and the next moment was fighting against Susharma's children, the Samsaptakas. On the twelfth day, Drona planned to capture Yudhishtira by engaging Arjun in a fight with the Samsaptakas but in a swift move, Arjun rescued his elder brother. That night, Duryodhana admonished the elderly Drona for his failure to prevent Arjun from rescuing his brother.

Dronacharya was very much hurt by

these words. This made him all the more determined to seize Dharmaraya and to gain victory for the Kauravas. He therefore re-arranged his army around Yudhishtira so that he could be easily captured while Arjun would be busy fighting against the Samsaptakas. This formation was called Chakravyuh, an extremely difficult maze and only Krishna, Arjun and his young son Abhimanyu knew how to break the maze. But Abhimanyu only knew how to get in.

Since Arjun and Krishna were away from the spot, the responsibility of penetrating the maze fell upon the young but valiant shoulders of Abhimanyu. He therefore told his uncle that they were to follow him. Yudhishtira at first hesitated but since there was no other option, he agreed.

With the blessings of his uncle, Abhimanyu drove his chariot and penetrated the maze. But the Pandavas were prevented from following Abhimanyu by Jayadrat, the king of Saindav. As a result, Abhimanyu was surrounded by enemies. He fought alone but could not withstand the attack for very long. Duhshyasana cut Abhimanyu's limbs one by one. Karna pierced the boy's body with his arrows. Jayadrat drove his spear through the inert body and finally killed him. The entire ground was covered with Abhimanyu's blood and the Sun also set, as if unable to witness the scene.

The Kaurava camp was overjoyed with Abhimanyu's death and on the other hand, the Pandava's army was plunged into sorrow. Arjun who returned to the camp after defeating the Samsaptakas was met with mourning

and immense grief. When he heard about the way in which his dearest son was killed, he swore. "Before the Sun sets tomorrow, I shall kill Jaydrata who was the cause of my son's death." In his grief, Arjun also accused Yudhishtira and Bhima of being irresponsible and having sent a youngster like Abhimanyu to penetrate the Chakravyuh. He could not even console his wife Subhadra and Uttara, Abhimanyu's wife.

News of Arjun's vow reached the Kauravas. Duryodhana was very eager to protect Jayadrata against Arjun by waging the war himself till the evening. There was a severe fight between the two stalwarts - Arjun and Duryodhana and none could gain an upper hand. The day was drawing to an end. Duryodhana thought that since Arjun could not keep up his vow to kill Jayadrat the same evening, he (Arjun) would, out of shame,

commit suicide. And victory would be Duryodhana's. To meet the situation, Krishna covered the rays of the Sun with his Hand and made it look as if the Sun had set. Jayadrata feeling confident that he had survived the day emerged out of his hiding and on Krishna's instructions, Arjun hit Jayadrata with his arrow chopping off his head.

The war continued even at night and when Bhima killed seven of Duryodhana's brothers, in retaliation, Karna used his Shaktya weapon on Ghatotkacha, Bhima's son and beheaded him. Ghatotkacha was the second son to die for the Pandavas.

When the war raged on for the fifteenth consecutive day, Krishna expressed his opinion that unless and until Drona was killed, the Pandavas would never be victorious. Hence he suggested to Arjun, "Arjun shout loudly

in the midst of the fighting that Drona's son Aswathama has been killed. The grief striken Drona will lose all his enthusiasm to fight and thus it will be easy for us to defeat him." Arjun did not like this idea of deceiving his Guru. Krishna then put forward this idea to Bhima. Bhima killed an elephant by name Aswathama and cried out aloud that Aswathama died. When Drona heard this, he at once knew that this was Krishna's trick. He therefore announced that he would believe his son to be dead only if the ever truthful Yudhishtira were to say it. So, at the instance of Krishna, Yudhishtira called out "Aswathama    Hatha    Kunjah" (Aswathama, the elephant, has been killed). Just as he was saying it, Krishna blew the conch so loud that Drona only heard that Aswathama ......... had been killed. Since Yudhishtira had uttered

these words, Drona took it to be true, threw down his weapons and sat down on the ground. His beloved son's death had robbed him of the will to live. Seizing this opportunity, Dhrishta-dyumna, in retaliation against Drona's humiliation of his father, drew out his sword and severed Drona's head.

On hearing the news about his father's death, Aswathama went berserk and brandishing his sword, attacked the enemy and killed many soldiers. He swore that he would wipe out the entire Pandava race to avenge for his father's death.

Drona's death doubled Duryodhana's grief. He then installed Karna as the Supreme-Commander. The war went on relentlessly with a great deal of death and destruction. There was intense fighting between Bhima and Dushyasana. Recalling what

Dushyasana had done to Draupadi, Bhima's anger exploded like a volcano. He leapt upon Dushyasana, lifted him up and using all his strength, thrashed him down. Bhima then tore Dushyasana's arm and sucked the blood from his body. Drithrashtra was grief striken when he heard about the gory way in which his son was killed. But it was too late to stop the war.

The sixteenth day of the battle witnessed Karna and Arjun confront each other. Shalya was Karna's charioteer.

The battle between Karna and Arjun was a clash of epic proportions.

Determined to kill Arjun, Karna used an arrow, which was a deadly weapon spewing serpents. As it was about to strike Arjun, Krishna pushed the chariot down into the earth by a few

inches. The arrow could only knock down Arjun's headgear. The arrow of serpents returned to Karna and wanted to be re-used on Arjun. But Karna recalled the promise made to Kunthi that he would not use the same weapon twice. Arjun was thus saved.

As fate would have it, Karna's chariot got stuck in the blood soaked mud. His charioteer Shalya refused to get down and lift the chariot up. "Karna, you have

so often boasted about your strength. Prove it now," He said in ridicule.

With no other alternative, Karna jumped out of the chariot and tried to lift the chariot single-handed. Arjun took advantage of the situation and poured a rain of arrows on Karna. "Please do not take undue advantage of me, O Arjun!" cried out Karna. "Have you forgotten the code of conduct that you cannot attack an unarmed man?" Red in face, Arjun hurriedly put down his quiver full of arrows. But Krishna laughed scorningly and said, "Yes, Arjun, have you forgotten that Karna was among those who hacked Abhimanyu to death? What was Karna doing when Draupadi, a defenceless woman was disrobed in front of everybody? Just don't waste your time. Don't lose this chance. Use your arrows upon Karna."

Arjun saw wisdom in Krishna's advice. He therefore used his arrows, one after the other, on Karna. Karna forgot all the mantras he had to utter before using any arrow.

Parasurama's curse was upon him. The generous Karna had already donated his armour and earrings to Indra. His strength had subsided. Since he had already used the Shaktya weapon to kill Ghatotkacha, he did not have a suitable weapon against Arjun. To add to his misfortune, the wheel of the chariot just did not budge.

Arjun used his most powerful arrow which instantly severed Karna's head. A glorious light emitted out of Karna's body and submerged into the Sun. The Sun God had taken away his valiant son. On witnessing this scene, Arjun realised that Karna was an extra - ordinary person. Instead of feeling happy, Arjun

felt bereaved. He returned to his camp in a subdued mood.

Duryodhana grieved over his dearest friend's death for hours. None of the surviving Kauravas could console him. He felt that a terrible vacuum had been created in his army with the deaths of Drona and Karna. Seeing his anguish, Kripacharya tried to advice him, "Duryodhana, at least now make peace with the Pandavas. Survive this holocaust and enjoy the rest of your life." Even at that moment, Duryodhana turned a deaf ear to the advice. He appointed Shalya as the General with orders to fight till the very end.

Shalya fell a victim to Yudhishtira's arrow on the eighteenth day of the battle. On the same day, the wicked Shakuni was killed by Sahadev and the surviving brothers of Duryodhana by Bhima. Only

Kripa, Aswathama and Duryodhana were left.

At this stage, Duryodhana belatedly realised that he could not escape from the enemies. So he hid in a pool of water.

The Pandavas reached the spot shortly, and challenged him to come out of his hiding. When he emerged out of

water, Duryodhana picked up his mace and fought with Bhima. Both of them were equal in strength and skill and the

combat raged for a long time. Bhima who found it impossible to knock down Duryodhana looked at Krishna who made a sign by slapping the thighs. Bhima recalled the vow he had made when Duryodhana humiliated Draupadi. When the Pandavas had lost the game of dice, Duryodhana had called Draupadi his maid and had taunted her to sit on his lap. The enraged Bhima vowed, "Duryodhana! I will kill you by breaking your thighs." Though such a method of killing an enemy was contrary to the rules of war, Bhima recalled the grave injustices meted out by Duryodhana and dealing a powerful blow with his mace he thrashed Duryodhana's thighs into a pulp. Howling with pain, Duryodhana fell down and Bhima kicked him hard on the head.

"Stop, Bhima", cried his elder

brother, "It is not right on your part to kick a king in the head." On hearing this, Duryodhana talking with great difficulty told his cousin, "Yudhishtira, you may have scored a victory over me. But don't forget that this is an unethical victory for you. Arjun hid himself behind a woman to defeat the great Bhishma. You uttered a lie to make Drona give up fighting. Karna was killed when he was unarmed. And now Bhima has broken the rules of the war and thrashed my thighs with a mace. After all these events, you have finally managed to call Bhima's act of kicking my head as Adharma (unethical). Let him do whatever he wants to. It will only belittle him. I am an emperor. I am not a coward. I shall die a brave death after waging the war. A valiant world is awaiting me. My kingdom is now yours. You have paid a heavy price to gain it. I

am doubtful whether it will bring you peace of mind."

Yudhishtira was filled with sorrow at the thought that his cousin was to die shortly. Krishna was nonchalant. The Pandavas returned from the battlefield in a state of melancholy.

Duryodhana battled for his life. This was a tragic story created due to his own greed. Aswathama who could not tolerate Duryodhana's condition vowed before him, "O Emperor! Do not think that you are the only one to hate the Pandavas. For, I cannot forgive them for their deception in killing my father, I shall avenge by beheading the Pandavas one by one." Duryodhana, even when he was in his deathbed, was delighted to hear this, "Go, Guruputra! I am appointing you as the General. Show me the dead bodies of the Pandavas before I die."

It was a dark and terrible night. Aswathama came to know that the Pandavas were fast asleep in their camp. Actually instead of the Pandavas and Krishna, the Panchalas, that is, Draupadi's five sons and Dhristadyumna had chosen to sleep in the tent. Without even bothering to look at their faces, Aswathama butchered all of them and hastened to Duryodhana's side. But by that time Duryodhana had already died.

In the morning Draupadi was inconsolable when she heard about the killing of her five sons. She went to Yudhishtira and told him that if Aswathama was not killed, she would commit suicide on the funeral pyre of her children. The Pandavas went in search of him and found him hiding in a place near the river. When he saw them approaching, Aswathama charged

a blade of grass with a deadly mantra and threw it towards them. They avoided the blade of grass but in order to wipe out their race, it tried to hit the womb of Uttara who was pregnant with Abhimanyu's son. Lord Krishna at once stopped the grass blade with his hand and thus protected Uttara's womb. Frustrated by this, Aswathama escaped to the forest. He was never to be seen again.

The battle of Kurukshetra was over but Yudhishtira did not find peace of mind in any way. While the entire Hastinapur mourned over the loss of their kith and kin killed in the war, Dhrithrashtra and Gandhari wept over the loss of their sons and Kunthi over Karna's death. The blind Dhrithrashtra had the misfortune of cremating his own children. But still he hated the Pandavas and especially Bhima. So, when the

Pandavas came to him to pay their respects, Dhrithrashtra embraced them one by one, without there being any love or affection in those embraces. When he was about to embrace Bhima, the wise Krishna pushed Bhima aside and placed a metal statue before the blind king. The blind but very strong king hugged the statue so tightly that it was reduced to pieces. He thought Bhima was dead but when he learnt the truth, he suppressed his anger and blessed the Pandavas.

When Kunthi told her sons that Karna was her eldest born, the grief striken Yudhishtira performed the funeral ceremony for Karna. The Pandavas also performed the last rites for all the other departed souls and bathed in the Ganga to atone for their sins. Subsequently Krishna took Yudhishtira to Bhishma who was still alive. The grand old man gave his

blessings for the coronation of Yudhishtira as the emperor of Hastinapur. He also advised the new emperor about the path of Dharma. Shortly afterwards, when the Sun was in the northernly direction, Bhishma invited death and breathed his last.

Yudhishtira ruled over Hastinapur well and his reign brought peace and prosperity to the citizens. The Pandavas looked after Dhrithrashtra and Gandhari with love, affection and respect. Yudhishtira even performed their last rites when they died. Krishna ruled over Dwaraka for thirty six years after the battle of Kurukshetra before he completed his avatar (incarnation).

These events created a detachment towards life among the Pandavas and Draupadi. They therefore crowned Parikshit, son of Abhimanyu as the emperor of Hastinapur and proceeded

towards heaven. A dog followed them and kept them company all along. When they reached the gates of heaven, the dog was not allowed entry. So, Yudhishtira and the others did not want to get into heaven and preferred to go to Naraka, the hell.

The Devas were pleased with the Pandavas for their love towards the animal and let all of them into heaven.

*This is the story of Mahabharata.*

*Vedavyasa, a great sage, dictated the Mahabharata to Ganesha, the elephant god. Mahabharata is an epic, also containing the Bhagavad gita. It shows to the young and the old alike, the path of righteousness, knowledge, justice and love.*

## EXERCISES

### I. ANSWER THE FOLLOWING QUESTION:

1. Why was Ganga throwing her babies into the river?
2. Why did Bhisma vow never to get married?
3. Why did Amba hold Bhisma responsible for her ill-fate?
4. Who were the Pandavas and the Kauravas?
5. Why did Dronacharya ask Ekalavya to give him his thumb?
6. How did Duryodhana save Karna from humiliation?
7. What happened when Duryodhana tried to burn down the Pandavas in the wax mansion?
8. How did Bakasura meet with his end?
9. Describe briefly the happenings at Draupadi's swayamvar.
10. How did Jarasandha meet with his end?
11. What was Sisupala's secret as revealed by Bhishma?
12. How did Duryodhana trick Yudhisthira into losing his kingdom in a game of dice?
13. Who rescued Draupadi from the evil intentions of Duhshyasana?
14. What happened when the Pandavas went to drink water from a lake? How did Yudhisthira save them?
15. How did Draupadi lead Kichaka to his death?

16. How did Arjun announce his arrival in the battlefield to his three gurus- Bhishma, Dronacharya and Kripacharya?

17. Describe the meeting between Kunthi and Karna.

18. What happened when both Arjun and Duryodhana went to Krishna to seek his help?

19. Describe the fight between Arjun and Karna.

20. How did Duryodhana meet with his end?

## II   WHO SAID THIS TO WHOM AND WHEN:

1. "You are from a warrior clan and still you do not know how to take out the ball from the well."

2. "Respected Sir, I am at your bidding. Whatever you want, I will give you."

3. "From now on, you are my brother."

4. "I ask for your weapon, the Shaktya."

5. "I cannot bear to live outside the forest."

6. "Whatever you have got, please share it among yourselves."

7. "Draupadi will henceforth be our maid. She is at our command."

8. "Answer my questions before drinking the water!"

9. "Why are you concerned about a total stranger?"

10. "Do your duty without desiring for reward or for fame."

✢ ✢ ✢